W9-BBH-214

THAT WE MAY LIVE

THAT WE
MAY LIVE

JAMIE L. WHITTEN

D. VAN NOSTRAND COMPANY INC.
PRINCETON, NEW JERSEY

TORONTO   LONDON

D. VAN NOSTRAND COMPANY, INC.
120 Alexander Street, Princeton, New Jersey (08540)
24 West 40 Street, New York, New York (10018)

D. VAN NOSTRAND COMPANY, LTD.
358, Kensington High Street, London, W. 14, England

D. VAN NOSTRAND COMPANY (Canada), Ltd.
25 Hollinger Road, Toronto 16, Canada

Library of Congress Catalog Card No. 66-31955

First Published August 1966
Reprinted December 1966

PRINTED IN THE UNITED STATES OF AMERICA

PREFACE

THIS book is the result of a long-standing concern over unjustified public fears of those invaluable chemicals called pesticides. This concern dates from at least as far back as 1958, when Congress was asked to appropriate $10 million to help cranberry growers for the losses they had suffered from a greatly inflated pesticide scare.

This alarm, as explained in Chapter 9 of this book, arose from a statement by a member of President Eisenhower's Cabinet that led people to believe that eating the berry might give them cancer. The statement, issued a few weeks before Thanksgiving, practically destroyed the cranberry market that year and seriously affected it for several years thereafter. In its passage through Congress, the measure to approve the payment to the cranberry industry came before the House of Representatives' Appropriations Subcommittee for Agriculture, of which I have been chairman for fifteen years. This incident and the hearings on the appropriation aroused

v

my awareness of the dangers that public fear has for
agriculture.

My concern was greatly heightened by the next
big public scare, which resulted from the publication
of Rachel Carson's *Silent Spring*. In this furor my subcommittee was asked to authorize millions of dollars
more for further research on pesticides and methods of
pest control. About $27 million was finally appropriated
for this purpose.

Later, in 1964, the subcommittee was asked to
authorize the payment of about $8 million to dairymen
whose milk had been dumped after new, ultrasensitive
methods of analysis had found pesticide residues in it.
These testing methods had been introduced with insufficient notice for alfalfa spraying schedules to be adjusted
to allow for them.

As a result of such involvement in pesticide questions I became aware that there was a sizable movement
at work aimed at severely curtailing or even eliminating
the use of pesticides. I saw that this campaign often
made broad arguments for drastic action against pesticides on the basis of a few isolated incidents, half-
truths, and omission of facts where they did not fit
preconceived theories. This made me afraid that an
aroused public opinion might stop the use of materials
that I had become convinced are absolutely essential to
our health and prosperity. And so I began to speak out
in defense of the role of pesticides.

Because of my activities in this area, the National
Academy of Sciences invited me to participate in a
traveling symposium on pesticides from November 15 to

22, 1964, and I accepted. We participants spent a full day each at the United States Department of Agriculture research facilities at Beltsville, Maryland; the American Cynamid Company's Agricultural Center near Princeton, New Jersey; the Taft Engineering Laboratory at Cincinnati; the Wildlife Laboratory at Denver; and the University of California at Davis. The tour ended with a presentation by the United States Public Health Service at San Francisco. At each stop leading scientists made detailed presentations and answered questions.

The information I gained from this symposium strengthened my conviction that pesticides are now an absolute necessity to our way of life and redoubled my resolve to communicate this conviction to the American public before serious harm is done. One outcome is this book.

Now, after more than two years of intense effort, in which I was nobly aided by the Research Service of the Library of Congress and by scientists in the various departments of government, I realize how gigantic a task I have undertaken and how many persons have helped me. I would like to pay tribute here to those scientists, in and out of government, whose untiring efforts keep us one step ahead in the constant fight against insects and disease, pests and pestilence, and to thank those who have given freely of their time in reviewing and correcting this manuscript.

I dedicate this book to the general public, consumer and producer alike, who I hope and trust will benefit from my efforts.

CONTENTS

CHAPTER 1

INTRODUCTION

IN the beginning, man spent all of his time providing for his creature needs: food, the means to keep his body warm, and shelter from his enemies as well as from the elements. With time he learned he could domesticate and use goats, sheep, cattle, and other animals, thereby obtaining a better living from less effort. Then began the hundreds of years in which man was a nomad, roaming the land seeking grass and feed for his animals and for himself.

After many, many years man discovered that he could till the soil, select and grow crops which in turn saved for him much of the time previously spent in his search for food.

For many centuries, and in some areas now, man— busy with the problem of obtaining from his labor enough with which to exist—had little time for other activities and showed little ingenuity and inventive capacity, either in improving the productivity of his crops or in the plows or instruments he used. Only in the last few hundred years has man had a real breakthrough in his struggle for a better life.

It is since man had time for research that he developed newer and more and more effective machinery for tilling the soil, for harvesting and processing his crops. It is only since man has developed better and more prolific varieties of crops for food and fiber; since he has developed synthetic fertilizers so as to provide the maximum food for his own crops; since his own food, clothing and shelter have become easily available; and even more recently when through the control of insects he has saved himself from illness and his food supply from destruction, that man has had time for all the other pursuits which make for our high standard of living. He has been unbelievably successful.

Thirty-five years ago there were no atomic submarines, no missiles, no satellites, no jets, no nylon, no television, no teflon, no dacron, no DDT, and no synthetic rubber. Nuclear fission itself had not been discovered; and miracle drugs were virtually unknown. Manned flights into the stratosphere were merely a dream and the "man on the moon" was only a phrase to indicate the impossible.

Today our knowledge of all these things has literally changed the face of the earth. Man today stands on the brink of controlling the air above us and the elements about us. The man who developed the atomic submarine [1] recently told me that in future wars the nation which controlled the bottom of the sea might well emerge the victor.

Ours is the only nation where the cost of food averages only 18 per cent of our disposable income— income left after taxes and other fixed costs. United Nations' reports show the average for certain other countries as follows: [2]

Canada	22%	Australia	23%	Japan	43%
Ceylon	51	Italy	43	France	31
Sweden	27	Korea	51	Yugoslavia	46
Gr. Britain	27	W. Germany	36	USSR (Est.)	50

Our estimated national income in 1965 was approximately $544.6 billion, of which $98.4 billion went for food.[3] Just think what would be our situation if an additional $51.2 billion of our gross income had to go for food, leaving that much less with which to purchase the products of industry and labor—as would be the case if it took 27 per cent of our income for food as it does in Great Britain. And if it took 50 per cent of our income for food as it does in the USSR, we would have $178.8 billion less for purchasing other goods and services.

We in this great United States have gradually increased our farm productivity until 82 per cent of our income is available for many items thought to be necessities, and for luxuries, too.

As we improve our production of foods and our high standard of living, helped greatly by those relatively few people engaged in agriculture, let us ponder the words of Jonathan Swift:

§

And he gave it as his opinion that whoever could make two ears of corn or two blades of grass to grow upon a spot of ground where only one grew before, would deserve better of mankind and do more essential service to his country than the whole race of politicians put together.

John L. Blake felt much the same as Swift on this score:

§

It is not known where he who invented the plough was born or
where he died, yet he has affected more the happiness of the
world than the whole race of heroes and conquerors who have
drenched it with tears and manured it with blood.

Yet, the truth is that other scientists, through years
of research and study, have helped as much to provide
that extra ear of corn and that second blade of grass
for human use by saving them from insects and diseases
as did those who developed new varieties and new
machinery. The important contribution of those engaged
in scientific pursuits entitles them to equal credit for
the great improvement in the well-being of much of
mankind.

If biological study and its application had not
flourished in the past, civilization would have been stale-
mated on an agricultural level with no spare energies
or talent for the industrial and scientific revolution.

Fortunately, the vast majority of our people do
have full appreciation of scientific study and its con-
tributions of the past, together with its promise for the
future. This majority recognizes our great dependence
upon the findings of research scientists for the future
and has the greatest admiration and appreciation for
scientists themselves.

The medical scientists, of course, have already
received well-deserved credit from the general public.
As we read of the great plagues of years ago, of the
great advances in medicine in controlling many of
them, such as malaria, we see clearly how medical men

have served humanity, but we sometimes slight the entomologists and other scientists who supported their work
by isolating the causes and by developing means of
controlling the fleas, rats, flies, mosquitoes, and other
carriers of these dreaded and deadly diseases.

As we take pride in our increasing life span, about
twenty years longer since 1900 and still increasing about
a half-year annually, we are prone to forget the major
contribution of pesticides, developed by our scientists,
to a plentiful and wholesome supply of food and our
protection from insect-carried diseases. Now that the
use of essential pesticides is under attack, it is time we
reminded an urban and recreation-minded people that
we cannot afford to tie the hands of the less than 8 per
cent of our population which feeds us, simply because
we have perfected testing methods which can isolate
traces of many elements, even to the point of isolating
one part in a trillion.

To be sure, there are hazards connected with human
invention and progress; but we do not condemn the
inventor or the user of the wheel because there are
thousands of casualties directly connected with vehicles
utilizing this device.

We know as man has lived his life, day by day
and year by year, throughout history he has continued
to change and to build for himself a synthetic environment. His clothing, his housing, his food, in fact, almost
everything about him is the result of his converting
natural elements into products useful to him.

NOTES TO CHAPTER 1

1. Vice Admiral H. G. Rickover.
2. *United Nations Statistical Yearbook,* 1964, pp. 8, 46, 47, 96, 106, 154, 166, 178, 281, 315, 336. Figures for Japan and West Germany also include expenditures for beverages and tobacco of 8 to 9 per cent.
3. Estimated national income: Economic Report of the President transmitted to the Congress, January, 1966, p. 222. *Food expenditure: National Income Issue* of *Survey of Current Business,* published by the Department of Commerce, released at the end of February, 1966.

CHAPTER 2

THE LAND'S BOUNTY

THE gloomy forecast of the Reverend Thomas R. Malthus in 1798 that the world's population would outstrip its food production seems to find confirmation in the fact that the poorer countries have increased their output only one per cent in the last decade. In most of them the population is rising more than 2 per cent *a year*.[1]

Yet the United States and a few other highly developed countries have been able to resist the trend. Between 1940 and 1965 the number of Americans rose from 131.7 million to 194.6 million, an increase of 47.8 per cent. But from 1940 to 1964 the amount of corn raised for grain jumped 61.4 per cent. Wheat output soared 59.3 per cent, and meat production climbed 60.6 per cent. The production of beef alone increased from 7.2 billion pounds to 18.4 billion pounds, up 155 per cent—but still it lagged behind consumption, which was 19 billion pounds in 1964, about 98 pounds per person.

The increases in production were achieved despite the fact that the nation's farm acreage was stable and its farm population dropped drastically, to less than 8 per cent of the total. One result of the production rise was that food prices rose much more slowly than personal income. The average family spends only 18 per cent of its income per person on food, while the figure for an underdeveloped country as heretofore pointed out is likely to be 50 or 60 per cent. Despite the shrinking farm population, agriculture remains the nation's largest industry. It employs eight times more people than the steel industry, nine times more than the automobile industry, and one and a half times the number that works in transportation and public utilities. In addition, it directly supports 10 per cent of our nonfarm population—those who supply the farmer with his needs and who process and market his products.[2]

One reason for the soaring output of American agriculture is the increase in farm mechanization. Just as World War I spurred the adoption of the tractor and the combine, World War II, with its demands and labor shortages, led to the widespread adoption of the combined harvester thresher and the cornpicker, increased use of the field forage harvester and pickup baler, and acceptance of the cotton picker. The role of electricity should not be ignored; in 1934, 11 per cent of the farms had power, today more than 98 per cent do. As one result, pumps carry water that hands once did. The nation's 3.7 million farms make use of some 4.5 million tractors. The tractors do the work of 22 million work animals that would consume the feed output of 76 million acres. Agriculture uses more petroleum products than any other American industry. The average value of machinery and motor vehicles per farm was $4847 in 1964, compared with $592 in 1940.[3]

Another reason for rising production is the wider,

wiser use of high-analysis fertilizers. Crops remove the elements from the soil that make it fertile—calcium, phosphorus, potassium, and nitrogen. Fertilizers restore this loss for future crops as well as increasing the current crop in some circumstances as much as 50 per cent. Simple tests can determine what the soil lacks, and fertilizers with just the right proportions of nutrients can be applied according to the results. One estimate puts the contribution of fertilizers to the postwar production increase at 20 per cent. That the United States has not yet achieved its full potential with fertilizer can be seen by comparing its performance in some crops with those of some other countries. The vast American wheat fields, for instance, produce about 25 bushels per acre; the small, intensively cultivated wheat fields of the Netherlands average 60 bushels per acre, and Western Europe as a whole averages 34 bushels.[4]

Improved varieties of crop plants is another major factor. One of the main research efforts of the United States Department of Agriculture and the state agricultural experiment stations is the development of more productive plant strains that are resistant to diseases and insect pests and are adapted to the climate of different regions. The almost universal use of hybrid seed corn in the United States is one of the reasons this country averages 60 bushels per acre, the highest average in the world.[5]

Improved practices and engineering are other contributors. These can be as simple as rotating crops, planting them on the right dates, planting them more thickly, or thinning them properly. They can be as ambi-

tious as irrigation—about 37 million acres were irrigated
in the United States in 1963, to get away from reliance
on the whims of the clouds for moisture as well as to
make use of fertile but arid lands. To take corn again
as an example, the earlier hybrid varieties would not
produce satisfactorily in the southern states. Further
research and new varieties met the needs. Today, with
the application of more fertilizer when planting, to add
more nitrogen in early summer, and by planting the
seed more thickly, the South boasts some of the highest
yields of all.[6]

Then there are pesticides. These are the chemicals
that kill insects, disease organisms, weeds, mites, the
tiny worms called nematodes, and rats. Each kind of
chemical has an appropriate name ending in "cide,"
meaning "killer"; insecticide, fungicide, herbicide, acari-
cide, nematocide, and rodenticide. Though examples of
most kinds of pest killers were in use before World War
II, they assumed major importance in agriculture at the
close of the war with the introduction of two products—
the insecticide called DDT and the herbicide called 2,
4-D. Many more pesticides have now been put into use.
They have become so essential that their loss would be
an incalculable blow both to the farmer and to the city
dweller who consumes his output, and to the general
health of all.

Now, if pesticides cannot claim credit alone for
the many remarkable advances in agriculture, nevertheless they can boast a major share. One of the best sum-
maries of the place of pesticides in modern agriculture
was prepared by the Subcommittee on Evaluation of

Pesticide-Wildlife Problems of the National Academy of Sciences' Committee on Pest Control and Wildlife Relationships. In a report issued by the National Academy of Sciences—National Research Council, the panel said:

§

> . . . without the use of chemical pesticides most fruits and vegetables would be much scarcer in the market and the prices of the meager quantities produced would be prohibitive. It is known from studies conducted over the years that 40 to 80 per cent of the apples produced without the protection offered by pesticides in many areas will be damaged by codling moth, and 60 to 80 per cent damaged by apple scab, plus an equal or even greater degree of damage by other insects or diseases. To this fruit damage must be added the destruction that would be wrought by wood borers, scale insects, and other pests that affect the trees.
>
> Without the benefit of pesticides, the yield of staple fiber, cereal, and forage crops could be expected to drop from 10 to as much as 25 per cent. Careful studies have shown that the omission of insecticide treatments resulted in reduction of cotton yields of 25 to 40 per cent.
>
> Agronomists have demonstrated quite conclusively that, in general, a given acre of land devoted to a specific crop is able to produce only so much dry matter in any given season. With weeds partially uncontrolled, crop yields are reduced in proportion, and with some weeds completely uncontrolled, yields may be practically nil.
>
> The rise in pesticide usage has been closely associated with and has paralleled the advances in farm mechanization. Thus, in these days of automation and labor-saving devices, pesticides must be regarded as chemical tools which are just as indispensable as mechanical tools in the production of agricultural crops. It would be economically unsound for farmers to abandon the use of pesticides. Capital investments in farms and farm equipment today are such that occasional complete or even partial crop failures cannot be absorbed.[7]

The widespread use of pesticides has faced a growing attack from groups of people who, in all sincerity, feel that the chemicals are a threat to man and his environment. These groups gained a formidable champion when Rachel Carson, a former wildlife biologist with a magic pen, produced a book called *Silent Spring*. As a notice that once appeared on a bulletin board at the University of California at Davis put it, "One controversial book has jolted us into reevaluating man's entire relationship within his environment."

Aspects of *Silent Spring* are examined in this book in Chapter 7 and other places. At this point I would merely like to point out that Miss Carson, who regrettably died in 1964, did not condemn pesticides outright. For instance, she said, "It is not my contention that chemical insecticides must never be used." She noted with approval an approach to insect control in Nova Scotia orchards that combined a minimum use of insecticides with biological methods.[8]

Silent Spring gained wide attention when published in serial form in the *New Yorker* magazine in 1962. A few months later it appeared in the bookstores. It reached the best-seller list immediately and stayed there for months. A leading book club distributed it to thousands of members. Conservation and nature groups quoted it like Scripture. Congressional hearings resulted from it. Influential government officials praised it and acted on it. The repercussions are still widely felt.

In all the controversy that has arisen since *Silent Spring* appeared, one seldom-mentioned effect fills me with apprehension. As is widely known, some insects develop a resistance to insecticides. Attempts to eradicate the housefly in the late 1940's failed because a few flies with a built-in tolerance for DDT survived and passed on this trait to their offspring. In the past this effect has not been so serious because a steady stream of new insecticides has been available. An insect resistant to one chemical may fall easily before another that is not necessarily more toxic or dangerous for man and other creatures.

But lately there have been indications that the flow of new products is tapering off. It takes years and millions of dollars in research and development to produce a new insecticide. Can it be that chemical companies are turning their attention to fields that show more promise of returns for less investment of time and money and that are less fraught with controversy? If this is so, is it possible that in time we will face a deadly insect foe against which we have no weapon?

NOTES TO CHAPTER 2

1. I am indebted for most of this analysis to Jay Richter, director, Agricultural Services, Consumers Cooperative Association, who presented it in an address at the annual meeting of the association in Kansas City, December 8, 1965.
2. Most of these United States Bureau of the Census and Department of Agriculture statistics appear in *The World Almanac and Book of Facts, 1966* (New York: *New York World-Telegram and Sun*).
3. E. G. McKibben and W. M. Carleton, "Engineering in Agriculture," in *Farmer's World: The Yearbook of Agriculture, 1964* (Washington: Government Printing Office), pp. 96–98.
4. W. L. Hill, "The Need for Fertilizers," in U. S. Department of Agriculture, *Farmer's World*, pp. 101–102; Orlin J. Scoville, Lewis B. Nelson, and Elco L. Greenshields, "Land and Advances in Technology," in U. S. Department of Agriculture, *Land: The Yearbook of Agriculture, 1958* (Washington: Government Printing Office), pp. 483–484.
5. Kenneth L. Murray, "Grain, a Basic Food," in U. S. Department of Agriculture, *Farmer's World*, p. 121.
6. Charles E. Kellogg, "Potentials for Food Production," in U. S. Department of Agriculture, *Farmer's World*, p. 60, Elco L. Greenshields, "Water Has a Key Role," in U. S. Department of Agriculture, *Farmer's World*, p. 78.
7. *Evaluation of Pesticide-Wildlife Problems*, Publication 920-A (Washington: National Academy of Sciences–National Research Council, 1962), pp. 4–5.
8. Rachel Carson, *Silent Spring* (Boston: Houghton Mifflin Co., 1962), pp. 12, 260–261.

CHAPTER 3

NEW WEAPONS IN
AN ANCIENT WAR

AT that moment when man learned to
domesticate animals and to use them for his own benefit
he altered the natural balance of all living things on
earth in his favor. Later, with his development of agriculture he further altered the balance of nature. As his
numbers have grown and as his skills have developed,
man has developed new ways to tilt the balance further
in his own self-interest. Man's development of chemical
combinations to control insect pests is merely one more
forward step in his steady progress towards controlling
his environment for his own well-being and comfort.

As is the case with all things new, there have been
misgivings about this use of chemical combinations to
control pests. These complaints and attacks bring to
mind the prejudices which prevailed at one time against
the metal plow. The iron or steel, it was charged, poisoned the soil. Later there was opposition to the use of
synthetic, or man-made fertilizers on the basis that they
were not "God's creation."

In the case of pesticides, in addition to specific
charges, it is also asserted that pesticides upset the
"balance of nature." This assertion is the underlying

15

theme of *Silent Spring* and is the declared subject of
a complete chapter. "By their very nature chemical controls are self-defeating, for they have been devised and
applied without taking into account the complex biological systems against which they have been blindly
hurled," the author says.

§

> . . . The balance of nature is not the same today as in Pleistocene
> times, but it is still there: a complex, precise, and highly inte-
> grated system of relationships between living things which can-
> not safely be ignored any more than the law of gravity can be
> defied with impunity by a man perched on the edge of a cliff.
> The balance of nature is not a *status quo;* it is fluid, ever shift-
> ing, in a constant state of adjustment. Man, too, is part of this
> balance. Sometimes the balance is in his favor; sometimes—and
> all too often through his own activities—it is shifted to his
> disadvantage.[1]

To repeat, what this argument ignores is the fact
that man departed from natural processes when he
domesticated his first animal and later when he first
planted a seed. Though racked by disease and doubtless
plagued by lice, primitive man changed the balance of
nature even more when he cultivated plants or crops.
Crops, if they can be called crops at all, grew in limited
quantities in scattered areas. When he undertook to
plant entire fields in a single crop man altered the
natural environment and created an artificial one. One
can realize how artificial by driving through corn or
wheat country, where vast fields of one densely growing crop are seen for mile after mile. Even a pasture
planted in grass is highly artificial. Producing crops as
we do today creates a condition that often leads to the

explosive spread of an insect or a plant disease. But only through intensive agriculture can a rural population that is less than 8 per cent of the nation's total population feed everyone, and only through enormous production can there ever be hope of feeding the world's rapidly expanding population.[2]

The Irish famine of 1845–1849 provides an illustration of what can happen when a crop is stricken by something against which man has no defense. This horrible episode in history, caused by a potato blight, has been strikingly described by Cecil Woodham-Smith:

§

> The green fields turned black almost overnight, and tubers, hastily dug, collapsed into stinking masses, and the fearful stench of decomposition hung over the land. Starvation was commonplace and public works were ordered to provide work for a famine-stricken Irish people.[3]

In the bitter winter weather both men and women had to go out to labor on public works. They were drenched with cold rain and swept with snow and gales. More often than not they were already starving. The number of deaths increased rapidly, and 5000 beggars roamed the streets of Cork.

The rot destroyed Ireland's basic food supply. More than a million people, about 12 per cent of the population, died from hunger. A million and a half fled their homeland; a million of them came to North America. Among them were the ancestors of our late President, John F. Kennedy.

A leading chemist of the period, Dr. Lyon Playfair,

was called in to help combat the potato disease. But neither he nor anyone else knew that the cause was a microscopic fungus, *Phytophthora infestans,* which can reproduce with lightning speed and destroy potato fields almost overnight. The disease, now known as late blight, remains a problem today, especially in humid weather. But for years bordeaux mixture has been known to give fairly effective control, and since 1945 a combination of a modern fungicide and DDT has led to a sizable increase in potato production. But Ireland knew nothing of these in 1845.[4]

In face of the unknown, the search for causes bordered on the fantastic:

§

> Where did the rot come from, people asked fearfully? Did it fall from the sky in rain, did it drop from the clouds, did it rise from the ground? Had the soil itself become infected?
> Wild suggestions were advanced. Had the potatoes become blighted by "static electricity," generated in the atmosphere by puffs of smoke and steam issuing from the hundreds of locomotives that had just come into use? Or was the disease caused by "mortiferous vapours" rising from "blind volcanoes" in the interior of the earth? Another school of thought blamed guano manure, consisting of the droppings of the sea fowl, which had recently become fashionable. From County Clare came a new theory; a field was partly covered with clothes laid out to dry and the covered portion escaped the blight—"this," reported the *Nation,* "proves that the blow came from the air." [5]

Though the provocation is much less, the parallels with today's blaming of all sorts of conditions, including a general run-down feeling, on pesticides seems obvious.[6]

Chemicals to kill insects are the best-known pesticides and have aroused the greatest complaints. They are used against creatures whose ravages have been recorded since earliest history. There are probably some two million kinds of insects, several times the number of all other animal species on earth. Many of these are harmless and many are even beneficial. Lady beetles (or lady birds or lady bugs) feed voraciously on destructive plant aphids and other soft-bodied insects, and parasitic insects help control other insects harmful to man. Bees are agents of flower pollination, necessary to the development of fruits and berries and other kinds of plants. Producers of some of these crops, blueberries for instance, hire beekeepers to bring their hives to their fields to improve the fruit set.[7]

Nevertheless, many insects are threats to man and his food supply. Losses due to pests, insects, and diseases run as high as 40 per cent in some countries. They eat, steal, or destroy a large share of everything that man grows or stores.[8]

To appreciate this fact fully, one need only look at the ravages of insects and the diseases they carry in other parts of the world where pesticides are little used. Considering for the moment only their competition for food, look at the Middle East, where desert locusts have been sweeping the semiarid lands for centuries, leaving ruined crops and starvation in their wake. In some areas of Pakistan heavy waves of locusts, caterpillars, and crickets have caused food losses as high as 80 per cent. In India it is almost impossible to keep grain in storage because of the depredations of weevils and the world's worst pest to stored grain, the khapra beetle, which has been trying to make its way into the United States.[9]

The distribution of cattle in Africa is primarily determined by the presence or absence of the tsetse fly. This dangerous insect and the diseases it carries are the major reason an African child, once weaned, may never again taste milk. The cattle tick and the warble or torsalo fly cause tremenodus losses to hides, beef, and milk production in Central and South America. In some of the most heavily infested areas mortality among calves may be as high as 70 per cent. In Argentina, some 50,000 calves succumbed in a recent year to the screwworm, an ugly parasite practically eradicated in this country. In many parts of the world the best fruit is so damaged by insects that no American consumer would accept it as a gift.[10]

Many crop pests have been with man throughout history, but many others have turned to crops from the wild comparatively recently. For instance, before the mid-nineteenth century one species of beetle was confined to the Rocky Mountain area. When people settled the region, they began to plant potatoes. Fields of potatoes provided an environment suitable for a rapid increase in this insect's numbers, and it spread far beyond its original home. By 1874 the insect, now known as the Colorado potato beetle, had reached the East Coast.[11]

Insecticidal chemicals have been used to stem insect depredations since before the dawn of history. One of the earliest was sulfur, which later was an element in many inorganic insecticides. The use of Paris green, an arsenical pigment, as an insecticide began about 1865. First used against the Colorado potato beetle, Paris green was so effective that for many years it was the most widely used agricultural insecticide. Lead arsenate entered the picture about 1892 and was developed for use against the larva of the gypsy moth.[12]

Oils, another prehistoric pesticide, regained wide use with the discovery of petroleum in the United States and the development of kerosene. Kerosene and other petroleum fractions came into use as insecticides about 1873. Along with soaps, detergents, and other adjuncts, they have been widely used.

Other ancient pesticides are the botanicals, which are derived from plants. Control of sucking insects with tobacco dust was discovered in 1763, and nicotine and other alkaloids have been intensively studied by entomologists. Pyrethrum, derived from the flower of a type of chrysanthemum, was found to kill insects about 1800 in the Near East. Scientists later succeeded in synthesizing some of its components and increasing its toxicity by adding synergists. Rotenone, derived from the roots of tropical plants, was discovered to be insecticidal in 1848. Both these botanical materials are in use today. They are toxic to insects and relatively safe for animals and people, but they lose their toxic property quickly on exposure to air.[13]

While the insecticidal uses of early chemicals were discovered accidentally, calcium arsenate was deliberately developed for this purpose. William C. Piver, associated as a young man with a campaign to promote the use of lead arsenate, conceived a theory that this material and Paris green, which contained copper, were poisonous because they both contained the element arsenic. He looked for something cheaper than the metals to bind chemically with arsenic, working secretly with materials he hid under his boarding-house bed to avoid arousing his landlady's wrath. He shipped his first batch of calcium arsenate in 1912, and the chemical soon was given a central role in the fight against the boll weevil that plagued cotton growers in the South.[14]

In the early 1920's all arsenical insecticides became the object of widespread public alarm because fruits and vegetables sprayed or dusted with them sometimes retained some poisonous residue. Research began immediately for removing or reducing residues on harvested crops and for developing safer insecticides. About this time the Department of Agriculture began to investigate many different kinds of organic compounds that might control insect damage.[15]

In this period William Hunter Volck developed a series of spray oils, including in 1924 the summer oils, as well as quick-breaking emulsions and, with others, sprays combining summer oils with poisons and emulsive oil products. Some of the botanical insecticides were also perfected.[16]

Before World War II the number of insecticide manufacturers in this country grew to 35, and the industry, cooperating with federal and state laboratories, developed their products' effectiveness with a wide range of crops and insects.[17]

Although the beginning of the era of organic pesti-

first

cides is usually dated from the war, several compounds
in this class were actually in use before then. Besides
the natural products already mentioned, there were syn-
thetics with long names describing their molecules that
were early known to be toxic to insects—for instance,
carbon disulfide, paradichlorobenzene, and naphthalene.
Thiodiphenylamine was introduced as an insecticide in
1935 and was used extensively as an internal control of
worms in livestock. Others being used then include
ethylene dichloride, ethylene dibromide, ethylene oxide,
and methyl bromide as fumigants; several organic thio-
cyanates as household sprays; phenothiazine as a deter-
rent to the apple-loving codling moth; azobenzene as a
greenhouse fumigant; and several dinitro derivatives of
phenol and cresol as dormant sprays for orchards.[18]

The age of organic pesticides might just as well be
called the age of DDT, however, because it is by far the
best known and, twenty-seven years after the discovery
that it kills insects, the most widely used insecticide.

The name DDT comes from the first letters of the
principal elements of the chemical name, *d*ichlorodi-
phenyl*t*richloroethane. Because it combines chlorine
with carbon and hydrogen it is called a chlorinated
hydrocarbon. It is manufactured from chlorine, benzene,
and alcohol, which react and combine to form the DDT
molecule. DDT was first described in 1874 by a German
chemist, Othmar Zeidler, but its insecticidal value was
first established in 1939 by Paul Müller, a scientist working for the dye company, J. R. Geigy S.A. of Basel,
Switzerland. The Swiss potato crop was threatened that

Development of DDT

year by the Colorado potato beetle, and the company gave Swiss entomologists a sample of DDT for testing. The pest was controlled and the value of DDT against other insects was soon proved. Dr. Müller's work won for him a Nobel Prize in 1948.[19]

Geigy shipped samples of DDT to the United States for testing in 1942. The positive results soon led to the importing of the insecticide on a commercial scale, and in 1943 it went into production in this country for use by the armed forces. Its success in controlling typhus in World War II is described in Chapter 4. After the war it won quick acceptance in civilian use.

Another chlorinated hydrocarbon is benzene hexa-chloride, or BHC, made by reacting chlorine with benzene in the presence of ultraviolet light. Michael Faraday, the English scientist, first made it in 1825, but its insecticidal action did not become known until much later. This effect was mentioned in a patent application for a method of chlorinating hydrocarbons by an American scientist, Harry Bender, in 1933, but no one seems to have picked up the idea. In 1941, A. P. W. Dupire in France applied for a patent on the use of the material as an insecticide and the following year F. D. Leicester in Britain made a sample that was found to be insecticidal.

Research into why benzene hexachloride kills insects led to the development of another major insecticide. BHC is made up of a number of isomers, molecules with the same number and kind of atoms in slightly different arrangements. The lethal effect was traced to one of these isomers, which is now marketed under the name lindane. Similarly, studies of DDT led to the development of other materials with related molecules, including methoxychlor, kepone, toxaphene, and TDE. Chlordane, invented in this country, is the name given a material manufactured by employing a reaction developed by two German chemists, Otto Diels and Kurt Alder, who won the Nobel Prize in 1950 for their work. [20]

These scientists have been honored in the names given to two of the newer synthetic chlorinated hydrocarbons invented in this country that stand among the most potent devised so far. The materials are called dieldrin and aldrin. Although their molecules are similar in structure, their chemical properties are different. However, it has been found that aldrin apparently changes to dieldrin in the field.[21]

Another important class of insecticides, the organic phosphorous compounds, grew out of research during World War II. A German chemist, Gerhard Schrader, discovered them while searching for more powerful agents of chemical warfare. Extensive development has led to the introduction of parathion, a remarkably effective pesticide for crops. Other widely used members of this class are malathion, diazinon, tetraethyl pyrophosphate, and Guthion. Most organic phosphorous insecticides are extremely toxic to warm-blooded animals, but once applied they generally decompose rapidly, unlike most chlorinated hydrocarbons, which break down slowly and are hence called "persistent." [22]

Even more recently, several insecticides of the class

known as carbamates, such as Isolan and Sevin, have appeared.[23]

Fungicides

Modern agricultural practice uses chemicals to control destructive plant diseases like the late blight of potatoes and other crops. Their use has stirred much less comment than that of insecticides, but the role of fungicides in particular is highly important. Many plant diseases are also controlled by insecticides, just as the human disease of malaria is controlled by attacking insects in which the disease organism spends part of its life cycle.[24]

Plant disease

Agents of plant disease were at work long before man appeared, as scientists have found in the fossil evidence preserved in rocks. Among the earliest written records of man are complaints about blights, mildews, and plagues. The Old Testament tells of plant diseases visited upon man to punish his sins. Three hundred years before Christ, Theophrastus, the father of botany, described many plant diseases we know today: scorch, rot, scab, and rust. The Romans propitiated a god of rust, Robigus. Later centuries experienced frequent outbreaks of plant diseases that caused famine and death.[25]

Man turned to inorganic chemicals long ago in search of something to stop such catastrophes. Before 1000 B.C. sulfur was known to avert diseases as well as insects, though it did not come into general use until 1800. As early as 1705 mercuric chloride was used as a wood preservative. In 1761 copper sulfate was used with mixed success to control bunt on wheat seed. The mixture of sulfur with lime to soften it was suggested by Weighton in 1814. The result, appropriately called lime sulfur, found its way into plant-disease control in 1902, when someone noticed that it controlled apple scab. By 1908 the scientist A. B. Cordley was recommending its use as a fungicide.[26]

The discovery of one important weapon against plant disease occurred in France about 1882. The story goes that some of the grapevines of a small vineyard grew near a public pathway. The passersby naturally could not resist the temptation to pick a few grapes as they passed. The owner of the vineyard, unable to prevent the pilfering with torrents of words or waving of hands, hit upon another method. He mixed some lime he had on hand with water and splashed the mixture over the vines by the path, threw on a little blue copper sulfate to make the result look more unappetizing, and posted a sign proclaiming, "Poison."

Later the vineyard was stricken by downy mildew. All the vines were destroyed except those splashed with the improvised mixture. Thus began the use of bordeaux mixture, though the textbooks give credit not to the vine grower but to the scientists who determined why the mixture was effective. The remedy remains in use in the grape industry and has saved potato crops and bananas from the dreaded Sigatoka disease.[27]

The use of organic mercury compounds as a fungicide treatment for seeds was introduced to the United States from Germany just before World War I. Formalin, the trade name for a solution of formaldehyde in water with a little wood alcohol, was in use before then.

For a time farmers relied on compounds of copper, sulfur, or mercury, but greatly improved organic fungicides developed since 1945 have now come into use.

One of these is chloranil. At first it was considered too expensive to use as a fungicide, but tests later showed that an investment of 70 cents per acre for treating pea seeds would give a return of as much as $21.25 at 1951 prices. Today nearly all seed peas in the United States are treated. A patent for another organic fungicide, alkyl dithiocarbamate, was issued in 1934, but it was almost ten years before this and similar fungicides became available to the public. Ethylene bis dithiocarbamates combined with DDT form the standard treatment to prevent late blight in potatoes. Quinones, imidazolines, triazines, and captan have also come into use. Organic fungicides have great potential value, particularly in the tropics, but their relatively high cost and the low income of many farmers in those regions have limited their use.[28]

nematocides

Mention one important class of pesticides to most people and all you will get is a puzzled look. This is the nematocides, chemicals that kill the destructive little pests known as nematodes, or eelworms. Though many times larger than one-celled bacteria, most nematodes are not quite big enough to be seen with the naked eye. In practice their effects are usually classified as plant diseases, with such names as root rot. Like insects they can transmit virus diseases, and they can aggravate other infections caused by fungi and bacteria. Their

effects are widespread on fruit and nut plants, vegetables, field and forage crops, lawns, and shrubs. One
guess is that they cause a billion dollars in damage to
American crops a year.

Nonchemical control methods, such as crop rotation
and letting fields rest for a time, have been practiced
for centuries, often without knowing why they helped.
But such methods are often impractical in modern
agriculture, partly because many nematodes have remarkable survival powers. The female of the golden
nematode of potatoes, for instance, becomes a tough
little cyst when it dies, and eggs inside may keep the
power of life for more than ten years. Some species enter
a dormant state when subjected to drying; one that
infests rye has been revived after a sleep of thirty-nine
years.

Carbon bisulfide was tested as a nematocide in
Germany about 1880, and in 1919 chloropicrin, the vom-
iting gas of World War I, was tried out for this purpose
in Britain. War-surplus chloropicrin began to find favor
in Hawaii for pineapple production in the 1930's, and
methyl bromide was introduced as a nematocide in
1940.

In the 1940's cheaper, more widely available
materials were found to act against nematodes. One,
called D-D mixture, is a by-product of the manufacture
of plastics and synthetic glycerin; the other, ethylene
dibromide, is added to leaded gasolines. In 1954 another
nematocide that is only slightly toxic to some kinds of
plants, DBCP, was released. Even better, more efficient

nematocides are being sought. The estimated consumption in 1961 was 100 million pounds, principally on tobacco, pineapple, and vegetable fields.

One of the most remarkable demonstrations of the value of nematocides involved cotton. A test plot without treatment for the pest yielded 203 pounds of seed cotton; a plot treated with ethylene dibromide produced 1605 pounds, an increase of 690 per cent.[29]

After thousands of years of warfare, there appears at last to be a weapon to lay low one of man's most formidable enemies, the rat. The weapon is Norbormide, a compound sold under the trade name Raticate. A result of a search for a cure for human arthritis at a pharmaceutical house, McNeil Laboratories, Norbormide is lethal to rats but apparently harmless to children, dogs, cats, poultry, even mice. Raticate has been sold a relatively short time, but already its effect has been highly praised by warehousemen and others who heretofore have been the victims of the rodent's appetite.[30]

Besides destroying, with the help of his cousin the mouse, an estimated $1 billion a year in terms of consumed and spoiled food, the rat is feared as a carrier of some of man's most dreaded diseases. It is no comfort to know that the rat is pest-ridden himself with fleas, lice, and mites, because the rat flea is the special agent— vector, scientists call it—of bubonic plague, the Black Death of the Middle Ages that decimated Europe time after time. The plague raged all over the civilized world from 540 to 590 A.D., killing as many as 10,000 people a day in Constantinople alone, and probably was one of the principal causes of the decline of the Roman Empire. In 1348 and 1349 it destroyed a quarter of the population of Europe. Between 1896 and 1917 it caused nearly 10 million reported deaths. Murine typhus is a disease of rats that the rat flea also transmits to man.

In epidemics, DDT and other insecticides have been used effectively in controlling the rat flea directly. In the most recent American outbreak, in Savannah, Georgia, in 1944 and 1945, DDT was credited with controlling murine typhus.[31]

Pesticides that eliminate rats are classified as rodenticides. Poisons that act against mice and field rodents also fit in this category. An effective rodenticide developed after World War II was Warfarin, an anticoagulant that produces painless internal hemorrhages. Rats and mice will eat it in bait without becoming poison-shy, as the wily rodents will of many other poisons, and it is easy to place Warfarin baits where rats can get them but other animals cannot.[32]

Though weeds are sometimes defined as "plants out of place," there is no doubt that their control is absolutely essential to a productive agriculture. Weeds compete with crop plants for water, food, space, and light. Though from the earliest times crude tools and hand pulling were used for weed control, today in regions where rainfall is high, these methods are insufficient to control infestations of such plants as nutsedge, quack grass, and field bindweed, even where labor is plentiful.

Practices that consume man's labor are clearly inadequate for weed control in a highly commercialized agriculture like that of the United States.

As with other pests, the use of chemicals for weed control began many years ago. Common salt was used in the last century and around the turn of the century such chemicals as copper sulfate and sulfuric acid came into use. But these materials kill all plants and can be used only on the spot where the weed grows or it may affect the crop plant as well. What was needed is something that kills weeds but not crops, something with selective action.

Certain dinitro dye compounds were found to affect some plants but not others in France in the 1930's, but chemical weed control did not become a reality until the discovery of the selective action of the phenoxyacetic acids in 1944. Within five years one of these chemicals with the jaw-breaking name of 2, 4-dichlorophenoxyacetic acid but with the catchy abbreviation 2, 4-D was being used to control weeds on more than 18 million acres of small grains and 4.5 million acres of corn in the United States.

By 1962 continued research had brought into use more than 6000 formulations of more than 100 organic chemicals in the United States. Herbicides are taking a larger and larger share of total pesticide sales; their use more than doubled in the short period from 1959 to 1963. They were applied to an estimated 85 million acres, 20 per cent of the nation's crop land, in 1962.

An example of a selective herbicide is propanil. This chemical, fortunately known by a shorter name than its proper one, 3, 4-dichloropropionanilide, does not injure rice, but is effective against barnyard grass and other annual weed grasses and sedges that often compete with cultivated rice. Reports from five states show that use of propanil has resulted in an average increase in rice production of 1000 to 2000 pounds per acre.[33]

New pesticides generally are developed in two different ways. One way is to study known pesticides, such as the known poisons produced by plants, in an attempt to unravel the chemical reasons for their action. The knowledge gained is then applied to developing new compounds with similar structures. The other way is to take many different compounds whose structure is already known and test them for effectiveness.

A classic example of the first method is anabasine, synthesized by C. R. Smith in 1928. Smith, a Department of Agriculture chemist, began work in 1922 on the nicotine molecule, for which no commercially feasible synthesizing process is known. After making, testing, and rejecting many compounds with similar molecular structures, Smith prepared one with the same number of carbon, hydrogen, and nitrogen atoms but in a different arrangement. It proved even more effective than nicotine for killing aphids.

The Department of Agriculture's use of the other method, screening thousands of compounds, later led to the development of phenothiazine as a pesticide. DDT and BHC were discovered in the same way.[34]

The procedures of a typical chemical company in

developing a pesticide can be divided into four stages. The first stage involves exploratory research. The second stage calls for measuring a potential product's activity and carrying out preliminary tests in the laboratory and in the field. The third stage is detailed and comprehensive research on performance, limitations, safety, and methods of production. The last stage confirms and extends the practical applications, leading to recommendation of the new pesticide by state and federal research agencies.[35]

After a compound has been synthesized in the test tube, the first step is to find out if it might be useful. The compound—one of more than 4000 tested by the manufacturer in one year—is tested with 50 different kinds of living things, including insects, fungi, bacteria, nematodes, rodents, and plants. Not only the chemical's killing power but its stimulating or growth-modifying effects are studied. With insects, the compound's attracting or repelling effect and its effect on reproduction are also observed. All data are carefully recorded for later processing by computer. Often the properties recorded in this stage have already been predicted, but sometimes new ones are discovered.

If the compound survives the first stage, it now enters a weeding-out phase designed to eliminate poor prospects before too much time and money have been invested in them. The chemical's performance at extreme conditions of light, temperature, moisture, and other forces of the environment are determined. The potential limitation of safety is also studied closely with laboratory animals. The effects on the eyes and skin, the effects of swallowing, the effects of single and multiple doses are observed in tests designed to determine the level of toxicity. Preliminary tests are also carried out with quail and chickens to help evaluate the effect on birds and with fish, snails, daphnia, and algae to determine the maximum tolerated concentration in water.

With data on performance, limitations, and safety and with a comparison with existing agricultural practices in hand, the third stage brings up the decision on whether the compound has a good chance of commercial success. A pilot plant is set up and a manufacturing process is refined. Extensive field tests are carried out in different regions of the country. Comprehensive safety studies include continuous two-year feeding tests in rats and dogs, feeding studies in chickens and quail, reproduction studies through two or three generations with rats and quail if applicable, tests on farm animals, and tests on fish and other water creatures, if applicable. These safety tests must begin early in the third stage so that the company will have the data it needs to register the chemical according to its timetable.

Other third-stage research bearing on safety deals with the residues a pesticide may leave on food for man. A major problem is simply to identify the residue, for it may undergo complex changes when exposed to the sun, rain, and air of a field or when consumed by a plant or animal. Radioactive tracers are used to tag the pesticide so that it can be followed through its history. If the residue has a different structure from that of the original chemical it must undergo tests of its own for such things as poisonous effect. The manufacturer must also develop highly sensitive methods of testing for residues so that traces as low as 0.01 part per million can be detected.

When a potential product has completed the third stage the project is already three or four years old.

If the company decides it wants to make and sell the product, the fourth stage begins. Samples are sent for testing to qualified investigators in state experiment stations across the country, the Department of Agriculture's Agricultural Research Service, the Fish and Wildlife Service, and the Public Health Service. The observations and criticisms of these investigators are a vital part of the process of determining the recommendations for use and the instructions on the label. The accumulated data form the basis for an application to the Department of Agriculture for registration and a petition to the Food and Drug Administration for determination of a tolerance. Once these have been granted the product is finally ready for the test of the marketplace.

By the time the company starts to receive income from the product, it will have spent five to seven years of time and $2 million to $3 million on research and development.

The Department of Agriculture has the responsibility for controlling pesticides under the provisions of the Federal Insecticide, Fungicide, and Rodenticide Act of 1947. The Food and Drug Administration has been given the responsibility for the safety of foods containing pesticides as required by the Food, Drug, and Cosmetic Act of 1938, as amended.[36]

All pesticides distributed and sold in the United

States must be registered with the Department of Agriculture. The department must see to it that all pesticide labels set forth the name of the product, the name of the manufacturer, a list of the ingredients, the weight or measure of the contents, the directions for use, and, when necessary, a warning statement which, if followed, will prevent injury to man, useful animals, and useful vegetation. The department is responsible for approving the use of pesticides not only on food crops but also on other agricultural products, such as cotton and tobacco, and for all nonagricultural uses, such as home gardening.

The department requires companies seeking to register a pesticide for use on food crops to describe the exact procedure and quantity to be used and to list each crop on which the pesticide may be applied. The scientific data gathered by the manufacturer throughout the development process must support the statements on the product's safety and effectiveness. The department itself is not required to test the chemicals for effectiveness and does not run its own residue tests, though it may field-test products later if it suspects that they leave unpermitted residues.

If the Department of Agriculture is satisfied that a pesticide will leave no residue on specified crops, it registers the chemical for use on those crops only on a "no-residue" basis. This provision has led to difficulties when new, ultrasensitive methods of detecting pesticide residues have been developed, as we shall see in Chapter 8.

If the pesticide candidate leaves a residue, the

Department of Agriculture notifies the company that the product will not be resistered until the Food and Drug Administration has established a finite tolerance or has specifically exempted the chemical from the tolerance requirement. A finite tolerance is the amount of pesticide that will be permitted on an agricultural commodity in terms of parts per million by weight. The department certifies to the FDA that the pesticide is useful and states whether the rate of application it has approved will leave a residue within the tolerance proposed by the manufacturer. After the Food and Drug Administration receives the petition, it publishes a notice in the Federal Register including the method of analysis the company has proposed for determining residues.

The agency studies the data submitted on the smallest amount of the pesticide that will cause observable ill effects on a range of test animals. It then relates this data to what might be expected with human beings in terms of body weight, then sets the tolerance at a hundredth of the result to provide a wide safety factor. The agency also studies the findings on the residues that result when the pesticide is applied as recommended, the maximum daily intake and the pattern of consumption of the food involved, the possibilities of someone's consuming extreme amounts of the food, and other factors that may be involved.

If the data submitted with the petition meet the legal requirements, the FDA establishes a tolerance, with a wide margin of safety, for residues on food. The Department of Agriculture, if it sanctions the FDA's action, then approves the label and registers the pesticide for marketing. The registration must be renewed every five years; meanwhile, the Food and Drug Administration continues to evaluate the product, and if it finds something that indicates a previously unsuspected health hazard it can lower the tolerance. The manufacturer also may apply for a higher tolerance or for establishment of tolerances for more crops at any time.

To enforce its tolerance limits the FDA has 18 laboratories in different parts of the country. The agency can seize shipments of any food product, such as milk or vegetables, that have residues exceeding the established tolerance. It can also seize shipments where any trace of a pesticide, within the limits of accuracy of the analytical procedure, is found in or on commodities where no finite tolerance has been set.

It may be seen that elaborate safeguards exist, and properly so, to protect the safety of the American people. As a result there has never been a known case of poisoning from residues of organic pesticides on food. While providing an unimaginable abundance of food that is more nutritious and free from blemish than any previously known, the nation's scientists, industry, farmers, and government have been vigilant to keep our food untainted.

NOTES TO CHAPTER 3

1. Rachel Carson, *Silent Spring* (Boston: Houghton Mifflin Co., 1962), p. 246.
2. Stanley A. Hall, "The Place of Insecticides," in U.S. Department of Agriculture, *Farmer's World: The Yearbook of Agriculture, 1964* (Washington: Government Printing Office), p. 114.
3. Cecil Woodham-Smith, *The Great Hunger* (New York and Evanston: Harper & Row, 1963), p. 101.
4. *Ibid.*, p. 44; Eugene S. Schultz, "Control of Diseases of Potatoes," in U. S. Department of Agriculture, *Plant Diseases: The Yearbook of Agriculture, 1953* (Washington: Government Printing Office), pp. 435–436; *Interagency Coordination in Environmental Hazards (Pesticides)*, Hearings before the Subcommittee on Reorganization and International Organizations of the Committee on Government Operations, U.S. Senate, 88th Congress, 2d Session (Washington: Government Printing Office, 1964), Part I, Appendix III, p. 787.
5. Woodham-Smith, *op. cit.*, p. 47.
6. For a rebuttal of the suggestion, see Chapter 5.
7. *Interagency Coordination*, Part I, Appendix I, p. 2; F. C. Bishopp, "Insects as Helpers," in U.S. Department of Agriculture, *Insects: The Yearbook of Agriculture, 1952* (Washington: Government Printing Office), p. 81; George H. Vansell and W. H. Griggs, "Honey Bees as Agents of Pollination," in U.S. Department of Agriculture, *Insects*, pp. 88–89.
8. Based on statement by Dr. George W. Irving, Director, Agricultural Research Service, Department of Agriculture, during hearings on 1967 Budget for U.S. Department of Agriculture, February 15, 1966.
9. Department of Agriculture Appropriations Subcommittee Report for fiscal year 1965, Rept. #1387, House of Representatives, 88th Cong., 2d Session, p. 8.
10. *Ibid.*, p. 9.
11. Hall, *loc. cit.*
12. *Interagency Coordination*, Part I, Appendix III, p. 783.
13. *Ibid.*, pp. 783–784.

14. Lea S. Hitchner, "The Insecticide Industry," in U.S. Department of Agriculture, *Insects*, p. 451.
15. B. A. Porter and J. E. Fahey, "Residues on Fruits and Vegetables," in U.S. Department of Agriculture, *Insects*, pp. 299–300.
16. Hitchner, *op. cit.*, p. 452; Louis Feinstein, "Insecticides From Plants," in U.S. Department of Agriculture, *Insects*, p. 222.
17. Hitchner, *loc. cit.*
18. C. V. Bowen and S. A. Hall, "The Organic Pesticides," in U.S. Department of Agriculture, *Insects*, p. 209.
19. Bowen and Hall, *op. cit.*, p. 210; Hitchner, *op. cit.*, p. 452.
20. Bowen and Hall, *op. cit.*, pp. 210–211; *Interagency Coordination*, Part I, Appendix III, p. 784.
21. Bowen and Hall, *op. cit.*, p. 211; Donald L. Kechely, "Agricultural Toxicology," *California Monthly*, July–August, 1963.
22. Bowen and Hall, *op. cit.*, p. 214.
23. *Interagency Coordination*, Part I, Appendix III, p. 784.
24. W. B. Ennis, Jr., and W. D. McClellan, "Chemicals in Crop Production," in U.S. Department of Agriculture, *Farmer's World*, p. 108.
25. E. C. Stakman, "The Role of Plant Pathology in the Scientific and Social Development of the World," in C. S. Holton, *et. al.* (Eds.), *Plant Pathology: Problems and Progress, 1908–1958* (Madison: University of Wisconsin Press, 1959), pp. 3–13.
26. "Insect Facts—To Aid Public Understanding of the Importance of Insects as Destroyers and as Man's Helpers in this 100th Year of Professional Entomology in the United States" (Entomological Society of America, 1954), Section 2, "Insecticide Application Methods," p. 4.
27. John C. Dunegan and S. P. Doolittle, "How Fungicides Have Been Developed," in U.S. Department of Agriculture, *Plant Diseases: The Yearbook of Agriculture, 1953* (Washington: Government Printing Office), p. 115; Ennis and McClellan, *op. cit.*, p. 109.
28. Ennis and McClellan, *op. cit.*, pp. 109–110.
29. *Interagency Coordination*, Part I, Appendix I, pp. 4, 16–17, 96–97; Appendix III, pp. 786–787; Ennis and McClellan, *op. cit.*, pp. 110-111.
30. Wheeler McMillen, *Bugs or People?* (New York: Appleton-Century, 1965), pp. 128–129.
31. Samuel W. Simmons, "The Use of DDT Insecticides in Human Medicine," in Paul Müller (Ed.), *DDT: The Insecticide Dichlorodiphenyltrichloroethane and Its Significance* (Basel and Stuttgart: Birkhäuser Verlag, 1959), II, 422, 430–437; Richard T. Holway, "Pesticides and Public Health in Pacific Areas," *BioScience*, Vol. XIV, No. 11 (Nov., 1964), pp. 20–21.
32. McMillen, *loc. cit.*
33. Ennis and McClellan, *op. cit.*, pp. 106–108; *Interagency Coordination*, Part I, Appendix III, pp. 785–786.
34. R. C. Roark, "How Insecticides Are Developed," in U.S. Department of Agriculture, *Insects*, pp. 200–202.

35. This section is based on an exhibit prepared by the Dow Chemical Company for the traveling symposium on pesticides of the National Academy of Sciences, presented at the American Cyanamid Company, Princeton, N. J., November 17, 1964. The material was drawn from a presentation before the Senate Subcommittee on Reorganization and International Organizations, October 9, 1963.

36. The regulations, procedures, and practices regarding pesticide registration are described here following the report of the investigative staff of the House Committee on Appropriations. The report, "Effects, Uses, Control, and Research Use of Agricultural Pesticides," appears in *Department of Agriculture Appropriations for 1966*, hearings before a subcommittee of the Committee on Appropriations, House of Representatives, 89th Congress, 1st Session (Washington: Government Printing Office, 1965), I, 165–208. The summary of regulations appears on pp. 170–171.

CHAPTER 4

GOOD HEALTH AND
A FULL LARDER

<!-- handwritten note in margin: DDT + Human Health -->

IN the summer of 1943, soon after Allied forces had swept into Italy, a case of typhus was confirmed in the dirty, crowded southern port of Naples. Neapolitans and Allied forces *alike* prepared for the worst. Since the Middle Ages, epidemic typhus has been the companion of war. Napoleon's retreat from Moscow can probably be ascribed to typhus as much as to freezing winter weather. The disease is caused by a microorganism borne by the body louse, which is little known where people bathe and wash their clothes regularly. But in war, soldiers must spend days and weeks without taking a bath or changing their clothing. In war, homes are destroyed, people live crowded and dirty in any hole they can find, sanitation breaks down. The louse follows as naturally as darkness follows sunset.

By the middle of December, 1943, 83 cases of typhus had been reported in Naples. By the end of the month the number had risen to 371. The dreaded epidemic had arrived. The stage had also been set for the debut of DDT in the protection of public health.

DDT had been shown in laboratory tests to be effective against the body louse and a 10 per cent pow-

43

der in pyrophyllite, a talc-like material, had been developed. One of its advantages was that it retained its effectiveness for weeks, killing any lice that might hatch after treatment as well as those caught when the dust was applied. It had checked a typhus epidemic in a test in a Mexican village and it had controlled lice in the people of North Africa. Naples was to be its first test in a full-scale epidemic in a war-ravaged city.

Dusting stations were set up all over Naples. Teams with hand and power dusters worked from house to house, dosing people, beds, clothing. Institutions received the same treatment, and in some of the larger hospitals and prisons dusting was a routine measure every two weeks. Corpses of typhus victims were dusted as well as mourning survivors. If a quick survey showed that less than 70 per cent of the people in a block had been treated, the whole block was dusted again.

By early February, 1944, the epidemic was broken. The number of cases in and near Naples was held to 1914. For the first time in history, a wartime typhus epidemic had been halted before it had run its normal course.

Thereafter, little 2-ounce cans of DDT powder went wherever the GI's and their allies did. No one seems to have worried about what effect possible residues in their tissues might have; it had been proved safe from toxic effect for use on the body and there were more serious threats to worry about. As the war in Europe sped on to its blazing end the use of DDT became routine, checking epidemics in liberated concentration camps and in protection of groups of wandering refugees and doubtless preventing much more. Later, in the Korean conflict, lice were found to have developed resistance to DDT and a new control material using pyrethrum and lindane was adopted. But if every other achievement of DDT is forgotten it will still be remembered for its control of typhus in World War II.[1]

As this historical example dramatically shows, the benefits of pesticides are not limited to one field. Public health workers the world over have used them to fight the most dreaded scourges of mankind. Farmers find them essential to assure high yields and outstanding quality in their crops. They are invaluable for protecting our forests and ranges from destructive outbreaks of pests. And they have a valuable place in the home, lawn, and garden, where most people gain their acquaintance with them. This chapter tells the story of pesticides in these four fields.

PUBLIC HEALTH

Epidemic typhus is only one of the diseases borne by lice—relapsing fever and trench fever are others—and the louse is only one of 10,000 kinds of little creatures, including insects, ticks, and mites, that infect man directly or indirectly with disease. Most of these do so only occasionally and incidentally, but many species of mosquitoes, flies, fleas, and mites stand out as more menacing disease carriers. At least 27 diseases, including some of the world's deadliest, can be controlled partly or completely by DDT and its allies.

Malaria, for instance, was once a serious problem

in the United States, but today it is practically nonexistent, largely because of antimosquito campaigns soon after World War II.

People commonly think of diseases as being caused by bacteria, which are a plant form of life, or viruses, which seem to be little more than protein molecules. Malaria, however, is caused by a tiny protozoan parasite, an animal form of life. Rampant in a man's bloodstream, it causes successive attacks of chills and fever. It may kill a person or it may debilitate him so that he can devote only a fraction of his normal energy to his work. It can subside only to return months later, even though no new infection has occurred.

The parasite has a complex life cycle that requires both human and Anopheles mosquito hosts. Though this mode of transmission is what made the disease so tenacious, it is also its weakness, for if a link in its life chain can be broken it is as good as wiped out. Thus if the number of people carrying the organism falls below a certain point, the disease is no longer endemic in the population and not enough mosquitoes will find enough infected people for the parasite to multiply. And, if the insect vector can be eliminated, malaria will die out of the blood of the people, for it can never complete an essential phase of its life nor be transmitted to another person.

By the eve of World War II, malaria, once widespread in this country, had been confined to the Southeast. But there it was a costly and enervating disease, striking 900,000 people and killing 4000 in one year as recently as 1935.

When I was a boy, in the hill section of Mississippi

on the edge of the Delta, it was known that the Anopheles mosquito carried malaria, but the people generally had not accepted the fact. Older people still thought that malaria was contracted from "miasma," the mist or fog that lies late in the afternoon over the sloughs and bayous of the Delta. They knew there was some connection between such places and the disease.

When I was about ten years old I contracted malaria and was unconscious, near death I am told, for several days. I carry scars now from quinine inoculations. Following the illness, I took quinine in chocolate syrup for a period that seemed like years, though perhaps it was only a matter of months. I suffered no recurrence of the disease, but my sister contracted another type of malaria and was subject to severe recurrent attacks for nine or ten years.

In the final attack on malaria, a federal-state eradication program was launched in 1947, aimed at both the parasites in human beings, which were vulnerable to war-developed drugs, and the vectors. The campaign made use of DDT's unusual residual powers, discovered and developed at the Department of Agriculture laboratory at Orlando, Florida, in World War II. Sprayed on a wall where mosquitoes rest, DDT kills the insects for weeks. The peak of the mosquito-control phase was reached in 1948, when the inside walls of more than 1.3 million homes in 360 counties were sprayed. By 1950 reported malaria cases were down to 2184. Eight years before there had been 58,781 cases—and 861 deaths.

Interestingly, one of the few flare-ups of malaria in the country since then occurred in 1952, when a Korean veteran on a camping trip suffered a relapse. Mosquitoes picked up parasites from him and transmitted them to a nearby girls' camp. The outbreak was quickly controlled, but such experiences indicate that there may be revivals of malaria introduced by returning veterans from Vietnam.[2]

Malaria has been wiped out in other large regions of the world. One of these is Italy, which had been so identified with the disease that she gave it its name (literally, "bad air"). Under a strong public-health campaign, malaria had been on the decline since the beginning of the twentieth century, but had staged a comeback during the war, from 55,000 cases in 1939 to 411,600 in 1945. Residual DDT spraying of human dwellings began in mosquito-infested areas in 1944. The decrease in malaria mosquitoes was spectacular. In one test carried out with a control area, a square yard of a wall in an untreated area harbored 185 mosquitoes and the average per square yard in a treated section was 0.06. The incidence of swollen spleens in people, a sign of malarial infection, also dropped. The Pontine Marshes, a deadly malarial region for thousands of years, soon was the home of 100,000 healthy people, and areas that had been regarded as submarginal became highly productive farmland. Malaria deaths have been practically unknown since 1948. Similar stories could be told for many other countries.[3]

Mosquitoes also carry yellow fever, or yellow jack, which used to strike terror in many parts of America. A deadly virus disease, now largely eradicated in our country, it still lurks in the jungles of South America and Africa, and since 1950 it has flared up in Panama and Costa Rica.

Dengue, or breakbone fever, a painful and debilitating virus disease, is also carried by the yellow fever mosquito. In 1922, Texas had more than half a million cases of dengue. At times in World War II this illness incapacitated large numbers of American troops on Guam and other Pacific islands.

Encephalitis, caused by several different viruses that attack the central nervous system, is transmitted by several species of mosquito. In the tropics mosquitoes also carry elephantiasis, a disfiguring malady in which the victim's extremities and genitals become grotesquely swollen because of small roundworms that hatch in the bloodstream and establish themselves in the lymph glands.

The housefly has shared man's food and bred in his waste for ages. Its filthy habits, its range of 13 miles or more, and its huge appetite make it one of the great carriers of disease. It has been known to carry typhoid fever and to contaminate food and utensils with organisms causing dysentery and diarrhea. Flies are believed to have a part in spreading the germs of cholera, yaws, trachoma, and tuberculosis. A cousin, the tsetse fly, carries the African sleeping sickness that affects vast areas of that continent. Rat fleas carry bubonic plague and murine typhus, discussed in Chapter 3 in connection with rodenticides. Ticks and mites—technically not insects at all but a class of arthropod called the acarids, kin to the spider—transmit scrub typhus, relapsing fever, forms of typhus and encephalitis, and other diseases.

They also cause irritating conditions of their own, such as scabies (by the itch mite) and chigger bites.[4]

An example of what can happen when vigilance against potential disease carriers is relaxed was provided by the encephalitis epidemic in Houston in 1964. Despite warnings by experts that trouble might be brewing, the area had no program to control its widespread mosquitoes. Then migrating birds brought in the virus of St. Louis encephalitis, named for the city where it first struck in this country in the 1930's.

A mother was stricken with the disease in 1961. The case was not properly diagnosed for months, and then it was forgotten. When more people began to fall ill and fill the hospitals in the spring of 1964 the disease at first was believed to be aseptic meningitis, which has similar but much milder symptoms. As the cases mounted the health department, because of faulty reporting, was unaware that an epidemic was brewing. Not until late in August, after blood samples of 78 victims, including 12 who had died, had been examined in Austin, was the disease properly diagnosed.

Finally the city rallied to its defense. Private exterminators, Boy Scouts, and volunteers sprayed mosquito-infested areas. Citizens lined up at fire stations with bottles, tin cans—any kind of container—to receive free insect repellent. Finally the epidemic faded, leaving a toll of 38 dead and 1000 seriously afflicted—many, since the disease strikes the central nervous system and the brain, crippled or mentally maimed. Moreover, a blood-sampling survey by the United States Public

Health Service showed that 250,000 people, a quarter of Houston's population, had symptoms.

A popular magazine described the sequel as follows in the summer of 1965:

§

> Nevertheless irate citizens have given orders. At a referendum last November they demanded that the menace of encephalitis-bearing mosquitoes be removed forever, and voted a million-dollar-a-year extermination and study program. The referendum, however, included all of Harris County, of which Houston is only a part. And there are mavericks among the county officials who disagree with the voters. Some feel the use of pesticide will "poison" the atmosphere. Others contend a mosquito-extermination program will be futile unless adjoining counties cooperate. And still others insist that "the results won't be worth the money." Whatever their objectives, these officials can—if they choose—slow down the program's timetable.[5]

AGRICULTURE

Today the American housewife can enter a supermarket and buy food for her family's dinner that is higher in quality than could have been imagined thirty years ago. At the fresh-fruit counter she can buy unblemished apples and grapes; at the vegetable section she can find potatoes without insects or blight or even sprouts; at the frozen food case she can pick up peas that taste better than if she had picked them in her own garden yesterday; at the meat section she can select the best government-graded beef. Sometimes she may grumble that the best cuts of steak are well over a dollar a pound, but if she stops to think she will realize that the cost of food has risen much more slowly in the last decade than her family's income.

Such bounty is the envy of the world. As we have seen, not all the credit for such abundance goes to pesticides. Nevertheless, they can claim a major and indispensable share. The economic benefits of pesticides to farmers and consumers alike are simply incalculable. Here too, there is hardly anyone in the world, let alone the United States, who has not received tangible benefit from the agricultural use of pesticides. Even the hungry of underdeveloped areas of the world are a little less hungry for this reason, for America has been able to share her own surplus with other people as well as help them make better use of their own agricultural resources.

Chemical insecticides are used to combat more than 10,000 species of insects that are always waiting to steal man's food wherever they have the chance—in the field, in the grain elevator, on the pantry shelf. Altogether they cost us at least $4 billion a year. Though the chemicals have given man an advantage in the conflict, the advantage is tenuous, for many insects have a capacity to develop resistance to a given insecticide. So far, man has maintained his advantage by developing new insecticides to use whenever older ones have faltered in effectiveness. In the 48 states, excluding Alaska and Hawaii, agriculture uses some 225 million pounds of control materials a year. About 14 million pounds of fumigants are also used for stored materials.[6]

Practically every crop has its own insect pests. Take apples, for instance. The United States produces more dessert and cooking apples than any other country: 2.8

million tons a year. Apples have the codling moth, which as a larva causes the unappetizing holes that once marred practically every apple. The moth's ravages have been so great in some areas that many orchards have been abandoned or destroyed. The Grand Junction, Colorado, section and northwestern Arkansas are examples. In one of the most recent tests of the value of insecticides on fruit, apple trees in West Virginia that had no sprays after the petals of the apple blossoms dropped showed 87 worms per 100 apples. On trees sprayed with Guthion, 100 apples turned up only three or four worms. And of course many other pests like apples as well as people do —for instance, the apple maggot, the plum curculio, orchard mites, and the San Jose scale. Many pests require control with different materials applied at different times, and the methods have to be changed from year to year and from region to region.[7]

Or look at corn. Of the world's annual production of 190 million tons, the United States produces half, about 95 million tons. American production has·risen despite a shrinking acreage; though many other factors are involved, the use of modern insecticides is a major reason. On sweet corn, the kind one buys for "corn on the cob," the most serious pest is the corn earworm, a little green caterpillar that later turns into a drab little moth. Consumers, naturally, demand corn without worms. In a test in Florida in 1957 and 1958, an untreated field produced an average of only 1.6 worm-free ears of corn per 100. The rate in a field treated with Sevin, a carbamate type of insecticide, was 86.2 per 100.[8]

The alfalfa weevil, a native of Europe, has been a pest in the West since 1904 and has spread rapidly in the East since 1951, apparently from another introduction. In many areas the growing season's first cutting of alfalfa would now be a total loss without insecticides. In a 1964 test in Maryland, malathion and methoxychlor applied 18 days before cutting increased the yield of the first and second cuttings from 1.6 to 2 tons per acre and the protein content from 16.9 to 20 per cent. An investment of $5 per acre yielded an increase of $20 in the value of the hay.[9]

Insects have a direct effect on farm animals, too. Anyone who has ever seen the misery that insects can cause to a cow might well advocate insect control for the same humane motives that concern him about accidental poisoning of wildlife. Perhaps they will welcome the fact that economic motives as well as humanitarian ones have led farmers to seek ways to reduce these kinds of insect pests.

One cattle tormentor is the horn fly, a bloodsucker about half as large as a housefly. Horn flies usually cluster on the back and shoulders of an animal and leave only to lay eggs in fresh cow droppings. In warm weather a new generation can appear as frequently as every two weeks, and if unchecked as many as 4000 may infest a single cow. The only way to control the horn fly is with such insecticides as toxaphene, methoxychlor, and malathion in the form of sprays, dips, and back-rubbers. In one test in Kansas, an insecticide caused beef cattle to gain as much as 15 pounds more a month than untreated animals.[10]

Similar benefits in terms of increased milk production have been proved for dairy cattle, which are pestered by a variety of biting flies by day and mosquitoes by night. An experiment in treating dairy herds in Illinois resulted in an increase in butterfat production of as much as 29.8 per cent.[11]

The crop that has long been the staple of much of the South and West, cotton, is the target of a wide assortment of insect pests, including lygus bugs, boll weevils, bollworms, and cotton fleahoppers. Long-range studies in three different states show not only the long-range benefit of insect control with cotton but document the marked improvement in control that occurred when DDT arrived on the scene. In Waco, Texas, treated plots yielded an average of 34 per cent more cotton than untreated plots from 1939 to 1945. From 1945 to 1958 the increase was 53 per cent. In Tallulah, Louisiana, where the test program began in 1920, the increase was 26.4 per cent before 1945, 41.3 per cent after. In Florence, South Carolina, the postwar increase was the greatest of all—from 23.6 per cent to 53.9 per cent.[12]

Small wonder that the cotton-growing Mississippi Delta region has one of the highest rates of pesticide application in the country. The Delta, an extremely fertile region on both sides of the Mississippi River, begins just below Memphis and extends 200 miles or more to the south. In the growing season hundreds of motor vehicles and aircraft apply tons of insecticides to the cotton fields, and other crops, such as wheat, oats, soybeans, and cover crops, receive less regular applications. The roar of spraying and dusting aircraft is as common

as the noise of tractors. Such treatments are absolutely
essential, for the warm, humid climate of the Delta produces an unbelievable number of destructive insects.
Yet the Delta, as shown in Chapter 6, nourishes a flour-
ishing wildlife population, and the Department of the
Interior is spending large sums in an attempt to get rid
of the swarms of blackbirds that blanket the area.

The harvest of a crop by no means marks the end
of the insect problem. In cereal grains, for instance, insects destroy at least 5 per cent of the world's production and degrade the quality of what remains. Various
weevils and beetles can cause the loss of as much as 10
per cent of stored grain in one season in the Great Plains
region, and in the deep South losses can run as high as
9 per cent a month. The chief foes have such names as
the saw-toothed grain beetle, the flat grain beetle, the
red flour beetle, and the Angoumois grain moth.[13]

The Department of Agriculture is fighting to keep
one of the world's worst pests of stored grain, the
khapra beetle, from gaining a foothold in this country.
The khapra beetle resists ordinary treatments. When it
is found, the storage area must be covered tightly with
tarpaulins and fumigated with deadly methyl bromide
gas. By 1962 a total of 671 establishments in the West
and Southwest had been treated. Interceptions at ports
of shipments of infested grain products also reached a
peak of 249 that year, from a level of 36 only five years
before.[14]

For the domestic pests, measures to reduce the
moisture content of stored grain and good, tight bins and
elevators are the principal means of control. Insecticides

have an essential place, however, in preparing an empty storage area to receive grain, for residual types are used to spray places where insects may be hiding. Fumigation with a volatile material that leaves no poisonous residue, such as carbon tetrachloride and ethylene dibromide, is usually practiced soon after the grain is put in storage.[15]

Members of a grain-handling study group that returned from the Soviet Union a few years ago reported that the Russians have had serious trouble with many insects and pests, including the klop cheropashka bug in the Ukraine and the Caucasus. This insect had reached pestilence proportions at the time of their visit. A Department of Agriculture study group that visited Russia in 1958 also noted, incidentally, that weeds were a major problem in most agricultural areas. These reports indicate that effective control of weeds and insects, especially in small grains, is still in its infancy in the Soviet Union.[16]

Control of crop insects also helps control another enemy, plant disease. Insects, particularly those that suck plant juices, like aphids and leafhoppers, carry most of the viruses that afflict useful plants. Insects also carry many of the bacteria and fungi, just as they spread many of the diseases of man. They can also promote a disease indirectly, by boring a hole in a stem through which a fungus can enter. Even the indispensable bee is at least partly responsible for the spread of the fire blight in orchards.

Diseases can spread many other ways, however—the wind, birds, animals, splashing water. They affect every plant crop to the tune of an estimated total of more than $3 billion a year. Control methods besides insecticides are necessary to combat these diseases.

The slightest carelessness on the part of a farmer can mean the loss of an entire crop and financial ruin. An example cited in the introductory chapter of *Plant Diseases: The Yearbook of Agriculture, 1953* is a poignant illustration. For some reason, a Pennsylvania farmer once decided to spray his apple orchard with materials that had not been tested and recommended by his state agricultural experiment station. The result: an attack of apple scab, a fungus that forms olive-green patches on the leaves and fruit. Not only was the harvest cut 80 per cent, but the trees were so badly weakened that yields were low for years afterward. To carry on the farmer had to borrow heavily, and eventually he took a full-time job off the farm. Similar examples could be found in almost any agricultural county in the nation.[17]

Few people realize today that Ceylon, the Indian Ocean island famed for its tea, once led the world in coffee production. But about 1870 the coffee-rust fungus invaded the plantations. No control method was found, and while Ceylon's planters turned to tea the world's coffee center shifted to Brazil and other South American countries.[18]

Agriculture attacks its disease problem a number of different ways. One of the main methods is to plant varieties of crops that resist the diseases. One of the best-known examples is sugarcane, which was practically destroyed in Louisiana in the 1920's by sugarcane mosaic. The introduction of resistant varieties from Java, followed by intensive breeding work, restored the crop as an important contributor to the agricultural economy.[19] The role of plant resistance and farming practices in controlling plant diseases are discussed further in Chapter 10.

In the important fungicidal method of control, chemicals are applied to plants by spraying, are used to treat seeds before planting, and are used to fumigate the soil. Some of the older fungicides, such as copper sulfate, are still in use, and some newer ones, like chlorinated phenols and thalamides, have won an important place. By controlling black rot in grapes, for instance, ferbam— ferric dimethyl dithiocarbamate—has increased the yield per acre from 1000 pounds to 8000 pounds. Used against leaf curl in peaches, ferbam raised the yield from 1 ton, classified as poor-cull, to 7 tons, 6 of which were rated good-fancy.[20]

Effective treatments for plant diseases caused by viruses and bacteria remain one of the principal goals of agricultural research. Antibiotics, so successful in controlling bacterial disease in man and animals, have had only limited success in plants, notably streptomycin, against fire blight of apples and pears. No effective control for virus diseases is known.[21]

The phenomenal growth of the use of herbicides in agriculture, outlined in Chapter 3, has taken place because farmers have found that it pays. This has been shown in various experiments using comparable test plots, one of which receives chemicals and one of which does not.

Applied to open permanent pastures, 2, 4-D in a Nebraska experiment increased the yield of forage plants per acre from 1100 pounds to 2800 pounds, or 254 per cent. In alfalfa, the herbicide CIPC increased the production in Maryland fields from 3000 pounds to 4600 pounds per acre. In one of the most spectacular results ever recorded for a controlled experiment, the chemical Dalapon was credited with affording such control of annual weeds that the yield of birdsfoot trefoil, a legume, rose 4825 per cent, from 80 pounds to 3860 pounds per acre.

Weed control in strawberries costs $30 an acre with chemicals, $200 an acre by hand. The comparable figures for cotton are $8 and $24. Chemical weed control has boosted the productivity of wheat, oats, and barley fields and of grazing lands by 10 or 20 per cent.

Fitting together the control methods for all the pests of a particular crop makes quite a complex spraying schedule. An example is the 1966 Extension Service schedule for sweet corn in a Northeastern state reproduced in the table on the following pages.

Herbicides find many uses outside of farm fields. They control noxious weeds that cause allergies and other ailments of humans. They are invaluable for controlling undesirable growth in ditches and other places where mowing is impossible. They are finding an important place in controlling the problem of algae and aquatic weeds that clog lakes, streams, and canals. In a test in the West, aromatic solvents controlled aquatic weeds in irrigation canals and ditches at a cost of $38.11 a mile, a saving of $330.31 over other methods.[22]

For want of a better home, a number of agricultural chemicals that do not actually kill plants are often included with the herbicides. These chemicals, including growth regulators, defoliators, and dessicants, find a wide variety of uses.

SPRAYING SCHEDULE FOR SWEET CORN
IN NEW JERSEY, 1966
INSECTS

Pest	Material	Notes
Nematodes	D-D, EDB, Telone, or DBCP	See Extension Bulletin 363
Seed corn maggot	Any commercial combination treatment	
Corn flea beetles	DDT or parathion	Repeat when beetles reappear. DO NOT use emulsifiable concentrates on small corn. Water-based emulsions of parathion can be used on small corn for flea-beetle control
Wilt	Control corn flea beetles according to insecticide recommendations	
European corn borer	DDT, Sevin, DDT-parathion, or DDT-malathion	Begin application when tassel comes out of whorl. Continue at 5-day intervals. See Special Note 1. DO NOT use Sevin after tassels appear (for bee protection)
Smut	See recommendation for corn borer control	Four applications at 4-5-day intervals when first tassels appear
Corn sap beetle	Malathion or parathion	
Corn earworm	TDE- DDT-parathion, DDT-malathion, or DDT	Mineral-oil-pyrethrum treatment can also be used. See section on preparation of baits, dips, and mixes, Special Note 1
Fall army-worm	See recommendations for corn earworm	

Crop Stage	Chemical	WEEDS Rate per Acre and Minimum Dilution	Suggestions
Preemergence	Atrazine	1½# (2# of 80% W.P.[a]) in 30 gal. water	Apply after planting and before emergence. One shallow cultivation at lay-by may be desirable to control late - germinating crabgrass. Banding 18″ over row decreases cost and reduces the amount of chemical that might carry over.
	DNBP (SINOX PE or PREMERGE)	4½-6# (1½-2 gal.) in 20 gal. water	Apply after planting but before seedlings appear. It may also be banded over 18″ of row using reduced amounts of chemical.
Emergence to 2″ tall	Atrazine	1½# (2# of 80% W.P.[a]) in 30 gal. water	Apply postemergence when weeds and corn are from emergence to 2″ tall. When this and other atrazine treatments are used, do not double-crop during this season. Cover crops following corn are satisfactory providing recommended rate of atrazine is not exceeded.
	DNBP (PREMERGE or SINOX PE)	1½-3# (½-1 gal.) in 20 gal. water	Apply when weeds are up or breaking and corn is emerging. Use lower rate when temperature is above 80° and when corn is up.

[a] W.P. = wettable powder

SOURCE: *1966 Pesticides for New Jersey* (New Brunswick, N. J.: Cooperative Extension Service, College of Agriculture and Environmental Science, Rutgers—The State University) pp. 50, 132.

Growth regulators have developed from F. W. Went's discovery of hormones in plants in 1928 and from

P. W. Zimmerman's discovery a few years later that some chemicals can affect plant growth in many ways. Such chemicals do not stimulate growth by providing more plant food, like fertilizers. Instead they control an aspect of the plant's life cycle. The effect can be stimulation of growth. Gibberellic acid is used in California, for instance, to increase the size of Thompson seedless grapes. But they can also retard growth where desirable. They can induce or retard sprouting. They can thin a fruit crop to increase the size of the remaining fruit, they can hasten maturation, and they can prevent fruit drop so that the crop can be harvested from the tree or bush rather than the ground. Their use has risen sharply; in 1940 they were applied to about 10,000 acres, today they are used on more than 800,000 acres of orchard and vegetable crops.

Naphthaleneacetic acid, for instance, is used to keep apples from falling before they are ready for harvest. Only one teaspoonful is used on an acre of apple trees, which produces about 200,000 apples. The quality of fruit picked from the trees rather than from the ground is much higher, and since higher quality fruit brings higher prices on the market the return on the grower's investment can be substantial. The consumer also gains.[23]

Defoliants and dessicants have found their chief uses in cotton fields, where the development of harvesting machines would have been almost impossible without them. Defoliants cause the cotton leaves to fall when the fiber is ready for harvesting. They can return $18 or $20 an acre under certain conditions where cotton is picked with the spindle types of machines. Dessicants also kill leaves, but the leaves, instead of dropping, wither on the stem. This action is considered an absolute necessity where the stripper machines are used. The savings with this type of harvester over hand picking run $27 to $33 per acre. Regrowth inhibitors are also used to keep new leaves from growing back before harvest.[24]

If potatoes are not stored at low temperatures they sprout and deteriorate. Cool storage is largely impractical for such a bulky product, however. Control of sprouting has been achieved with such unpronounceable growth regulators as chloroisopropylphenylcarbamate (CIPC).[25]

Other types of chemicals are needed to preserve the quality of fruits and vegetables between the time they are harvested and the time they reach the dinner table. Such chemicals benefit the grower and the distributor who save by not losing so much through spoilage. They also help the consumer, who receives a better product for less money because the larger total market supply results in lower prices—assuming that the demand level is the same, as elementary economic theory teaches us.

For instance, a recent round-up estimated that the chemical known as Dow A is used on all Florida oranges packed in polyethylene bags at the shipping point. In seven days this chemical reduces the proportion of oranges affected by decay from 25 per cent to 7 per cent. Another compound, biphenyl, is used on most lemon shipments and nearly all exported oranges and grapefruit. On domestic shipments biphenyl is believed to reduce decay and spoilage of lemons from 10 per cent to 5 per cent, and the saving is even greater in shipments abroad. In terms of the value of the fruit the annual saving is in the millions.

As another example, practically all of the California grapes shipped annually are fumigated with sulfur dioxide. If they were not, the rate of decay in an average ten-week storage period would rise from 4 per cent to 36 per cent, tests have shown. This would result in a loss of 192,000 tons of the annual 600,000 tons shipped.[26]

Considering the intensive use of pesticides where farm economics makes this feasible or necessary, such as orchards and cotton fields, it is understandable that fears should arise over the long-range effects of chemicals in the soil. Many people remember that several decades ago it was found that repeated applications of arsenical compounds in fruit-growing regions led to a considerable buildup in the ground, and that sometimes this damaged or killed the trees. The suggestion later that water running off farm land had carried enough pesticides into the Mississippi River to produce massive fish kills (see Chapter 9) also aroused uneasiness over whether residues might find their way far beyond the fields where they were laid down.

To find out the facts, the Department of Agriculture is setting up 55 or more testing stations throughout the nation to monitor pesticide residues in soils, sediment, water, crops, livestock, fish, and wildlife. Several of these stations are in areas where the Public Health Service is studying the extent of human exposure to pesticides in the environment; coordination of these research efforts should produce highly fruitful results in an area where few facts are known.

Though conclusive findings will not be available until the program has had a chance to mature, the Department of Agriculture has already announced that the first year's operation of a pilot study for the project in the Mississippi Delta showed no progressive buildup of pesticides in soil, sediment, or water.

In an address before the Entomological Society of America in New Orleans on November 29, 1965, J. W. Gentry of the Department's Plant Pest Control Division disclosed that pesticides have not built up even in cotton fields that have received relatively large amounts of chemicals for several years. DDT and its products were widely detected in water and sediment, but at quite low levels.

In one area, Mr. Gentry reported, a level of 1.3 parts per million (ppm) of DDT was found in a cotton field where 30 pounds of the chemical had been applied per acre over the nine previous years.

Another area had received 13 applications of endrin each year for eight years. The average application was 0.21 pounds per acre. The endrin level in the soil was only 0.05 ppm.

In 55 sediment samples taken from surface water sources, the average endrin level was 0.10 ppm. In the water itself, a fraction of a part per billion (ppb) was detected in surface waters at only one time, August, though in January, after heavy rains, a level of 6.7 ppb was recorded in quick-runoff water.

"Throughout the study," Mr. Gentry told the entomologists, "numerous other examples of the lack of large
buildup of organic pesticide residues in the soil, water,
and mud in the test area were found."

DDT in the water was well below the 1 ppb level
everywhere except in quick-runoff samples, where up
to 2.6 ppb were found, Mr. Gentry reported. The highest
reading in a sediment sample was 1.4 ppm.

Mr. Gentry further reported:

§

> In three study areas, endrin has been used for the past
> several years for cotton insect control. . . . From ten to 15
> pounds of the material have been applied per acre on a cumu-
> lative basis in each area. The disappearance rate of this insecti-
> cide from treated fields is particularly noteworthy. Residue levels
> in soil samples collected from June, 1964, to January, 1965,
> averaged 0.05, 0.08, and 0.33 ppm by area. It should be
> pointed out that the material was being applied to the fields
> during part of the sampling period.

There is much here, surely, to reassure us that the
integrity of the nation's soil and water resources is not
being undermined by heavy use of agricultural chemicals.

FORESTRY

The average American seems to have gained a firm
impression that the nation's forests are drenched every
year with the most potent insecticides, wreaking havoc
in the fish and wildlife populations while leaving insect
pests virtually untouched. This impression is wrong.
Foresters by and large love wildlife as well as anyone
and are deeply concerned with its protection. Forest

spraying programs are generally undertaken with extreme reluctance and only after all avenues of action have been explored. Great care is taken to minimize losses of fish and wildlife. And, when adopted, spraying programs are generally effective.

Far from being drenched, only 5 per cent of the forests of the 50 states has ever been treated with pesticides. The 1.2 million forest acres sprayed in 1962, a typical year, amounted to only 0.3 per cent of the total forest area. Only a few areas have ever been sprayed more than once.[27]

The precautions ordered by Secretary of the Interior Stewart L. Udall on his department's 550 million acres of public lands in September, 1964, had already been practiced there for years, except the injunction to "avoid using compounds which are known to concentrate in living organisms, such as DDT, chlordane, dieldrin, and endrin." The order gave priority to nonchemical control methods, avoiding contamination of bodies of water, and safe application procedures.[28] Such practices are also the rule on the national forests under the jurisdiction of the Department of Agriculture's Forest Service, except that the service believes the benefits of persistent chlorinated hydrocarbons far outweigh the disadvantages.

Why cannot the balance of nature be allowed to operate in our forest lands? Wouldn't this bring living things into a state of harmonious adjustment, with one element of the environment acting to check excesses of another without the need for toxic chemicals? The experts themselves say no, for nature often goes out of balance and permits sudden hordes of insects to defoliate

many thousands of acres of woodland, crippling its capacity to shelter wildlife and its attractiveness for man's recreation. A forester at Bitterroot National Forest writes:
§

> About 100 years before Lewis and Clark passed through western Montana in 1805, a large fire or a series of large fires burned about 1 million acres that later became portions of the Bitterroot, Deerlodge, and Beaverhead National Forests. In this burn, a lodgepole pine stand became established and eventually flourished. The stand became overmature and in the late 1920's was struck by a bark beetle epidemic which killed between 65 and 90 per cent of the stems.[29]

This is surely a prime example of nature out of balance, showing what can happen when forest pests are not controlled.

Probably the most widely distributed and destructive forest insect in North America is the spruce budworm. It is found from Virginia north to Labrador, west across Canada and the northern United States to the Pacific, and south into northeastern California and southern New Mexico. With a history of destruction dating from pre-Revolutionary days, this insect currently endangers large forest areas of the Northwest. Before the development of organic insecticides, outbreaks covering thousands of acres of spruce and fir often occurred in a single season. One DDT spraying at a cost of 76 cents per acre now can suppress such outbreaks.[30]

The gypsy moth, established in the Northeast after it was accidentally released by an amateur entomologist in 1869, eats 25 to 100 per cent of the leaves on trees over wide areas. This kills or retards the growth of trees, or makes them easy prey for disease and attacks by other insects. Though the gypsy moth is one pest for which a widely acclaimed biological control has been developed, its depredations continue. Timber destruction by the pest was reported to have increased significantly in Connecticut in 1964 when fear of pesticides curtailed spraying operations. Current federal-state control efforts are aimed at preventing its spread to other sections of the country.[31]

Several hundred thousand forest trees are killed each year by the various kinds of bark beetles. Many of these losses result from the boring of adults and the feeding on inner bark tissue of larvae. Many other losses result from the spread of fungus diseases, like the Dutch elm disease. Such forestry practices as removing diseased wood and culling the members of susceptible species are widely practiced, but the use of insecticides is essential.

What can happen when a bark beetle is neglected was shown in Colorado in World War II. Wind storms knocked down thousands of trees in stands of virgin Engelmann spruce on the White River Plateau. With manpower and money in short supply during wartime, the potential of the felled trees for breeding beetles was neglected. The result was a population explosion of the Engelmann spruce beetle that destroyed 500,000 acres of forest and 5 billion board feet of spruce timber before it was controlled with insecticides. The affected area is now a ghost forest and a major fire hazard.[32]

An antibiotic fungicide has been found that saves

the white pine, one of the nation's finest lumber trees, from the blister rust. Before 1958 the only known control method was to destroy the carrier host, the Ribes bush, and the disease was spreading over wide areas of the West. But in that year the new weapon was perfected and millions of infected trees have been saved at an average cost of 24 cents each.[33]

When a pest strikes a forest it is not trees alone that are lost. Destruction of timber eventually results in severe damage to property, soil, and water supplies. Trees and underbrush are essential to effective protection from floods and preservation of water-supply reservoirs. Defoliation of wooded areas not only reduces the soil's water-holding capacity and contributes to erosion but ruins recreation areas. Furthermore, defoliation increases the danger of fire, which not only destroys wildlife directly but also by consuming the plant and animal life on which it feeds.

An exceptionally clear statement of the problem appears in a report by Neal M. Rahm of Missoula, Montana, a regional forester of the Forest Service:

§

In our advanced economy we can no longer manage and protect vast areas of natural resources without chemical pesticides.

Insects and disease take a greater timber toll today than fire and must be attacked equally hard. Failure to do so will result in a reduced lumber supply in the immediate and more distant future and will impair State and local economies.

In Region 1 we are losing 300-400 million board feet of timber each year because of insects and disease. The Christmas tree business has been sharply curtailed because of spruce budworm devastation.

The Forest Service most certainly would be drawn and quartered if it walked away from burning forest fires which threatened an equal volume of timber. Disregard for insect epidemics is equally negative. Recommendations are prevalent that we revert to a stone-age culture and let disease and insects have the Douglas fir, white pine, and spruce. . . .

Montana's tremendous forest recreation values are also threatened. Dead and dying trees are rapidly increasing fuel masses on important watersheds.

Use of various pesticides is being vigorously questioned; yet some have been in use for over 25 years in household, garden, and agriculture sprays. All must be used with care and have been used without impairment of human health.

After 100 years of use, doctors still cannot tell us why aspirin kills pain. They know that it is toxic and kills some people, particularly children, each year. But we have not abandoned aspirin. We use it carefully, follow instructions, and keep it out of the reach of children.[34]

Two officials of the Forest Service, W. V. Benedict, director of the Division of Forest Pest Control, and W. L. Baker, assistant director of the Division of Forest Insect Research, have provided an illuminating explanation of the uses of pesticides in forestry. Insecticides, they point out, are not the only pesticides required; silvicides (tree killers) are used to eliminate a stand of unwanted trees, fungicides help control tree disease, noxious weeds are reduced with herbicides, and repellents and rodenticides keep animals away from plantings and young trees. These chemicals present little hazard, since a person usually applies them directly or, in the case of a repellent, the material coats a buried seed. Insecticides, however, are usually widely applied by aerial spray and attract more public concern.[35]

The forestry officials, like ecologists and other experts concerned with the misuse of pesticides, point out that the presence of a potential pest in limited numbers does not necessarily mean that it is about to multiply into an infestation. "Every year hundreds of known insect infestations and disease infections subside without becoming serious or doing significant damage," they write. "These are usually brought under control by natural factors, such as parasites, predators, disease pathogens, or weather." Moreover, most insects are harmless and some are beneficial.

Nevertheless, foresters must keep an eye on potential troublemakers, for some quirk of the weather or slight shift in another environmental condition that usually keeps them under control may fail, loosing a ruinous wave of pests. Where it appears that a serious infestation is in the making, the Forest Service begins a formal study of the problem. This includes a biological analysis of the prospects for damage and the control measures that might be required. Sometimes an outbreak is watched for several years before its magnitude can be determined. If it seems that a pest will seriously damage a forest, the service assesses the value of the resource at stake and the costs of control. The impact of the pest on various values of the forest—timber, wildlife, recreation, water, scenery—are considered in this economic analysis. Mr. Benedict and Mr. Baker point out:

§

The results of these analyses are taken into consideration in deciding whether or not to conduct a control project. . . . Evaluations are as penetrating and thorough as it is possible to make them. It is only when the evidence indicates that anticipated benefits exceed costs, that all requirements for effective control can be met, and that any serious pitfalls or damaging side effects can be adequately compensated for with proper safeguards that a control proposal is prepared.

Often pest outbreaks that seem serious to some are not sprayed because control plans fail to meet all these requirements. For instance, no large-scale operations have been taken against the elm spanworm, a defoliator that has been active in the southern Appalachians for several years, because it is not believed likely to cause enough damage to justify extensive aerial spraying. Infestations of spruce budworm in northern Minnesota and the black-headed budworm in Alaska have not been attacked because of the possible risk to fish. In another case, a spraying project was stopped only a few days after it started when entomologists reported that a sudden increase in a predator of the pest could be expected to achieve control.

A major public spraying program is reviewed by a variety of groups and experts on the state and local level as well as in Washington before it is begun. Forestry and health officials at all levels, wildlife biologists, and other interested groups are consulted. The plan goes before the appropriate Forest Pest Action Council, an advisory body open to anyone interested in each of the country's forest regions. At the federal level the proposal must clear the Forest Service's national office and go before the Federal Pest Control Review Board, which includes representatives of the Department of Agriculture and several other departments.

The Forest Service stresses forestry practices that will prevent pest infestations. Removal of trees that are past maturity or weakened by disease eliminates the breeding grounds of some insects, such as bark beetles. And the service is pressing research into other control methods that do not use pesticides. When pesticides are used, the type of chemical, its formulation and dosage, the method of application, and the potential hazards are carefully worked out and tested in small-scale field experiments. In aerial spraying the usual rate of application is a gallon of formulation per acre, and most of the fine mist comes to rest on the leaves of trees and shrubs, not the ground. Unless it is unavoidable, non-forested areas are not sprayed.

HOME, LAWN, AND GARDEN

Though most pesticides are sold for use on the farm, by far the greatest number of people encounter them in their homes and gardens. Pesticides have found many uses there, and while some are poisonous, there is no reason not to use them with proper caution if they are needed.

The array of fly sprays and similar products in the supermarket can be bewildering. Besides, recommended uses for different chemicals vary from state to state, particularly in outdoor uses, and as time passes older products may lose effectiveness or new ones may prove to be better. Anyone with a pest problem can find help at his county agricultural extension service. This office, staffed by the experts commonly known as the county agent and the home agent and their assistants, have the latest information from the U.S. Department of Agriculture and the state university. They are there to help everybody, not just farmers. Once a person knows what to look for, the problem of finding the right pesticide becomes quite simple. A list of available government publications on a subject like home gardening can be obtained on request from the Superintendent of Documents, U.S. Government Printing Office, Washington, D. C. 20402.

As one example of a recommended use, a problem with the common pavement ant, a medium-sized brown or black type, can be solved with chlordane, which is sold for household use as a 2 per cent solution or emulsion. This can be painted in a 6-inch swath along the baseboard, using an ordinary paintbrush. Chlordane is a poison; it must not be used on table tops or counters where food is handled and must not be used in a sprayer indoors. But when applied as directed, it presents no hazard to people or pets after the liquid has dried and will remain effective against ants for three to six weeks.[36]

Anyone who has ever had trouble with cockroaches may have been dismayed to find that they shrug off an ordinary household spray unless thoroughly drenched. A chlordane treatment similar to that for ants will take care of the long-winged American cockroach, but his cousin, the German cockroach, has developed resistance to this product. For this pest diazinon, a new phosphate insecticide, is effective at a concentration of 0.5 per cent. Here, too, no spray may be used in open indoor areas. The only place a sprayer may be used is into openings in walls. Insecticide may also be squirted under baseboards, a favorite cockroach haunt, with an oil squirt gun.

The cockroach needs plenty of water, so a simple step like fixing leaky faucets may help discourage the pest. Ordinary measures to keep food out of its reach also help. Needless to say, keeping screens in good repair and sealing any openings to the outside will help keep out unwanted insect visitors. Such practices will usually make pesticides unnecessary.[37]

House plants, like farm crops, are subject to a variety of pests. Several insecticides, including chlordane, DDT, Kelthane, malathion, pyrethrum, and rotenone, may be used as a dip or a spray. The pests they will control include ants, aphids, cutworms, mites too small to see without a magnifying glass, mealybugs, millipedes, and thrips.[38]

A popular outdoor planting for homes is the rhododendron. Nicotine sulfate, lindane, DDT, or malathion may be used to control a variety of pests that specialize in this ornamental, including lace bugs, borers, leaf miners, spider mites, scales, and caterpillars.[39] The family that raises vegetables in the back yard may use similar insecticides, and fungicides as well, but preferably in dust form applied when the air is still. It is, of course, essential to read the directions on the label. It is always a wise precaution to wear clothing that covers most of the body when using pesticides, for several of them can be absorbed through the skin. And one should always be sure not to spray into the wind.[40]

The herbicide 2, 4-D and its near relatives are not harmful to man or animals and are effective against the so-called broadleafed weeds but spare lawn grasses. The main problem with a material like this is that any drift may damage desirable plants, such as woody shrubs and flowers. Other types of weed killers may be poisonous, and, on general principles, all should be treated with the same respect as insecticides.

NOTES TO CHAPTER 4

1. Samuel W. Simmons, "The Use of DDT Insecticides in Human Medicine," in Paul Müller (*Ed.*), *DDT: The Insecticide Dichlorodiphenyltrichloroethane and Its Significance* (Basel and Stuttgart: Birkhäuser Verlag, 1959), II, pp. 400–419.
2. *Ibid.*, pp. 251, 340–343; F. C. Bishopp and Cornelius B. Philip, "Carriers of Human Diseases," in U.S. Department of Agriculture, *Insects: The Yearbook of Agriculture, 1952* (Washington: Government Printing Office), p. 147.
3. Simmons, *op. cit.*, pp. 257–263.
4. *Ibid.*, p. 253, 369–371; E. F. Knipling, "The Control of Insects Affecting Man," in U.S. Department of Agriculture, *Insects*, pp. 486, 491.
5. Ben Merson, "How a City Faced an Epidemic," *Good Housekeeping*, CLX, No. 6 (June, 1965), pp. 81 ff.
6. *Interagency Coordination in Environmental Hazards (Pesticides)*, hearings before the Subcommittee on Reorganization and International Organizations of the Committee on Government Operations, U.S. Senate, 88th Congress, 1st Session (Washington: Government Printing Office, 1964), Part I, Appendix I, p. 2.
7. *Ibid.*, p. 65.
8. *Ibid.*, p. 69.
9. This is unpublished data, furnished to the Agriculture Appropriations Subcommittee, containing research by Dr. Al Steinhauer, University of Maryland, and Dr. C. C. Blickenstaff, Entomology Research Division, Agricultural Research Service, U.S. Department of Agriculture.
10. *Interagency Coordination*, Part I, Appendix I, pp. 80–81.
11. *Ibid.*, p. 81.
12. *Ibid.*, pp. 63–64.
13. R. T. Cotton and Wallace Ashby, "Insect Pests of Stored Grains and Seed," in U.S. Department of Agriculture, *Insects*, pp. 629–630.
14. *Interagency Coordination*, Part I, Appendix I, pp. 116–117.
15. Cotton and Ashby, *op. cit.*, pp. 631–636; R. T. Cotton, "Fumigating Stored Foodstuffs," in U.S. Department of Agriculture, *Insects*, pp.

345–346; Robert D. Chisholm, "Nature and Uses of Fumigants," in U.S. Department of Agriculture, *Insects,* pp. 331–339.

16. Based on "Grain Marketing in the Soviet Union, With Emphasis on Wheat," Economic Research Service, USDA (Washington: Government Printing Office, June, 1961), p. 19, and "Crops Research in the Soviet Union," Report of Technical Study Group, Agricultural Research Service, USDA (Washington: Government Printing Office, August, 1959), p. 12.

17. Jessie I. Wood, "Three Billion Dollars a Year," in *Plant Diseases: The Yearbook of Agriculture, 1953* (Washington: Government Printing Office), p. 1.

18. *Ibid.,* pp. 7–8.

19. George H. Coons, "Breeding for Resistance to Disease," in U.S. Department of Agriculture, *Plant Diseases,* p. 181.

20. John C. Dunegan and S. P. Doolittle, "How Fungicides Have Been Developed," in U.S. Department of Agriculture, *Plant Diseases,* pp. 117–118; *Interagency Coordination,* Part I, Appendix I, pp. 90–93.

21. W. B. Ennis, Jr. and W. D. McClellan, "Chemicals in Crop Production," in U.S. Department of Agriculture, *Farmer's World: The Yearbook of Agriculture, 1964* (Washington: Government Printing Office), pp. 108–109.

22. *Ibid.,* pp. 107–108; *Interagency Coordination,* Part I, Appendix I, pp. 3–4, 82–86.

23. *Ibid.,* p. 101; Ennis and McClellan, *op. cit.,* pp. 111–112.

24. *Ibid.,* p. 112; *Interagency Coordination,* Part I, Appendix I, pp. 98–100.

25. *Ibid.,* p. 107.

26. *Ibid.,* pp. 105–106.

27. *Department of Agriculture Appropriations for 1966,* hearings before a subcommittee of the Committee on Appropriations, House of Representatives, 89th Congress, 1st Session (Washington: Government Printing Office, 1965), I, 169.

28. "Stringent Rules Ordered in Using Pesticides on Interior-Administered Lands," Department of the Interior news release, September 4, 1964.

29. John Morrison, Fire Hazard Management," *Fire Control Notes,* Vol. 25, No. 2, April, 1964.

30. *Interagency Coordination,* Part I, Appendix I, p. 108.

31. *Ibid.,* pp. 156–157.

32. *Ibid.,* pp. 108–109; F. P. Keen, "Bark Beetles in Forests," in U.S. Department of Agriculture, *Insects,* pp. 688–694.

33. *Interagency Coordination,* Part I, Appendix I, p. 109.

34. "What's Happening in Forestry," July 1, 1964, statement by Regional Forester Neal M. Rahm in *A Report to Private Forestry Enterprise,* Albert G. Hall (*Ed.*), (Washington, D.C., 1954).

35. The rest of this section is taken from W. V. Benedict and W. L. Baker, "Pesticides in Forestry—A Review of Current Practices," *Journal of Forestry,* May, 1963, pp. 340–344. The procedures outlined are very

similar to those recommended in subcommittee on Policy and Procedures for Pest Control, Committee on Pest Control and Wildlife Relationships, *Pest Control and Wildlife Relationships—Part II: Policy and Procedures for Pest Control* (Publication 920-B; Washington: NAS–NRS, 1962).

36. John B. Schmitt and Louis M. Vasvary, *House Ants and Their Control* (Extension Bulletin 348; New Brunswick, N. J.: Extension Service, College of Agriculture, Rutgers—The State University, n.d.).

37. John B. Schmitt, Louis M. Vasvary, and B. R. Wilson, *Cockroaches and Their Control* (Extension Bulletin 335; New Brunswick, N. J.: Extension Service, College of Agriculture, Rutgers—The State University, n.d.).

38. George V. Johnson and Floyd F. Smith, *Insects and Related Pests of House Plants . . . How to Control Them* (U.S. Department of Agriculture Home and Garden Bulletin 67; Washington: Government Printing Office, 1960).

39. Charles H. Connors, *Rhododendrons and Their Kin* (New Jersey Agricultural Experiment Station Circular 575; New Brunswick, N. J.: College of Agriculture, Rutgers—The State University, n.d.).

40. L. B. Reed and S. P. Doolittle, *Insects and Diseases of Vegetables in the Home Garden* (U.S. Department of Agriculture Home and Garden Bulletin 46, rev. ed.; Washington: Government Printing Office, 1961).

CHAPTER 5

ARE PESTICIDES A
HAZARD TO MAN?

IN 1962 a shocking event occurred in a Bing-
hamton, New York, hospital. Seven newborn infants died
when a widely used chemical was accidentally added to
their formula. Was the chemical arsenic, strychnine, or
one of the highly toxic organic insecticides? No; it was
common salt, added to the formula under the impression
that it was sugar.[1]

This regrettable incident illustrates one fact that
physicians and experts on the effects of poisons empha-
size over and over in any discussion of the question of
the danger of pesticides: Any substance can be poisonous if consumed in large enough quantities. Furthermore, everyone consumes small quantities of naturally-
occurring substances that are often considered poisonous
in practically every meal.

No one has made this point better than William J.
Darby, chairman of the Department of Biochemistry
and director of the Division of Nutrition at the Vanderbilt University School of Medicine in Nashville. In the
hearings conducted in 1963 by Senator Abraham Ribicoff of Connecticut and a Senate subcommittee, Dr.
Darby said:

81

§

[M]any substances which occur naturally in common foods are regularly ingested without evidence of harm. Among such toxic materials are solanine in potatoes; other saponins in soya, beets, spinach, peanuts, calabash, tomatoes, oranges, and so forth; oxalates in spinach, rhubarb, and so forth; giotragens in turnips, kale, cabbage, rape; arsensic in shrimp and oysters; antitrypsin in beans; phytic acid and phytates in a variety of foodstuffs; cyanides in cassava, almonds, and so forth. . . . The use of foods containing these is such that the toxic substance is ingested at an amount which we would define as a "permissible level" if we were considering a food chemical purposely incorporated into the food or a pesticide residue. . . .

The natural state of a foodstuff does not assure wholesomeness as is so often implied by misled faddists. Indeed, we possess much more information on the biologic role of most chemicals added to foods than we do on such naturally occurring components, even those which may become injurious.[2]

Such information is not cited here to frighten anyone away from eating the fish, potatoes, nuts, and so on, that he normally enjoys. It is merely to put into perspective the whole question of the effect of tiny amounts of pesticide residues in the diet.

At the outset of this discussion, let it be said emphatically that many pesticides are highly poisonous to man. They are not to be used indiscriminately. Some are dangerous even if they merely come in contact with the skin, for the skin absorbs them. Great care must always be exercised when using them to see that the directions on the label are followed to the letter. They should be stored where children cannot get at them, preferably under lock and key.

That said, let it be added that pesticides are safe when properly handled. No one should avoid household sprays for fear that a minute whiff will send them into convulsions or cause some apparently unrelated disease years later. Pesticides go through extraordinary tests for safety, and except for a rare allergic reaction, poisoning results only from a large exposure such as a suicide attempt or a major accident.

The extraordinary tests for safety that DDT underwent while it was being developed during World War II have generally been forgotten. Not only animals but human volunteers were fed the insecticide. Scientists from the Food and Drug Administration and the Public Health Service, working at the Department of Agriculture laboratory at Orlando, Florida, gave a man a dose of 500 milligrams (mg) of DDT without ill effect. This was the equivalent of only about 17.5 thousandths of an ounce, but for a chemical of the insect-killing power of DDT it was quite a dose. Later the scientists gave the same man about 27 thousandths of an ounce, again without harm.

Later tests have shown that some people will feel ill after consuming 10 mg per kilogram (kg) of their weight—about 0.16 thousandths of an ounce per pound, or 24 thousandths of an ounce for a 150-pound man— and that convulsions occur frequently when the dosage is 16 mg/kg or greater. People have recovered in a surprising number of cases where DDT was substituted for flour in pancakes and the like. But there is no question that DDT can cause death. The *Journal of the American*

Medical Association in 1951 listed 23 cases of DDT in-
gestion, four of which had resulted in deaths. Of the
total, 15 were suicide attempts.[3]

One of the world's leading experts on the effects
of pesticides on man is Wayland J. Hayes, Jr., chief of
the Toxicology Section, Technology Branch, of the Communicable Disease Center in Atlanta. One of the main
functions of the center, which is under the Public Health
Service, is to study the effects of pesticides on people.
Dr. Hayes has written or co-written more than forty
papers and articles on the subject since he began work
on pesticides in 1949.

In testimony before the Ribicoff hearings, Dr. Hayes
said that deaths by insecticide poisoning had been stable
at a rate of 1 per million population since the present
method of counting such deaths was adopted in 1939.
He continued:

§

There was no significant change in the rate of poisoning when
DDT was introduced experimentally in 1942 and commercially
in 1946. . . . The introduction of a wide variety of other new
pesticides beginning about 1946 was accompanied by no increase
in the rate of fatal poisoning. The rate for all accidental poisoning in this country has been about 2 per 100,000 for the last 25
years. This rate is about half that for acute poisoning as reported
between 1900 and 1910.

Citing figures of the National Office of Vital Statistics, Dr. Hayes said that on the average 10 per cent
of the deaths from solid and liquid poisonous substances
were attributed to pesticides. The proportion is smaller
in cities and is not increasing. As late as 1956, and

probably even now, more than half of the pesticide deaths were caused by compounds older than DDT, and more than half of the deaths were of children.[4]

By comparison, there are more than 48,000 auto deaths a year, more than 19,000 from falls, more than 2400 deaths by fire arms, and more than 215 from accidental drinking of poisonous types of alcohol.[5]

An exhibit Dr. Hayes introduced into the record of the Ribicoff hearings was a report of the National Clearing House for Poison Control Centers of the Public Health Service. The report showed that about 90 per cent of the cases of poisoning reported to it involved children under five years of age. Of the children's cases, 21.8 per cent involved aspirin. Pesticides were implicated in 5.3 per cent of the reports. Other products listed included bleach, 4.4 per cent, and detergents, soaps, and cleaners, 4.3 per cent.

Aspirin, the report said, accounts for nearly a third of the poisoning deaths of small children reported yearly.[6]

California is often cited in reports on the effects of pesticides because the state's farm workers are covered by workmen's compensation and their claims make good source material for statistics. California also uses fully 20 per cent of the nation's pesticides, but it accounts for only 7 per cent of the nation's pesticide deaths. Although only 13 per cent of the state's pesticide consumption occurs outside agriculture, half the pesticide deaths are nonagricultural.[7]

Dr. Howard Cann, former director of the National Clearing House for Poison Control Centers, has shown that a relatively high percentage of the nation's pesti-

cide poisonings occurred among children in the Southeast and along the Mexican border. In 48 per cent of
the cases the materials had been removed from their
original containers—often, apparently, taken home by
illiterate farmhands in milk and soda bottles.[8]

In California, an average of ten accidental deaths
a year have occurred from pesticides since 1951, most
of them small children. Arsenic caused over half the
children's deaths, but such tragedies have declined since
1961, when the state barred sodium arsenate, a fifty-
year-old pesticide, from use in homes and gardens.
Organic phosphates and methyl bromide caused more
than half the workers' deaths.[9]

Other California statistics show that of 83 on-the-
job deaths of farm workers in 1962, all but 7 were
caused by an injury such as a fall from a tractor. In the
period 1955 through 1962, only 4 deaths of farm workers
were attributed to pesticide poisoning, compared with
11 from heat stroke, 4 from tetanus, and 10 from mis-
cellaneous causes.[10]

More than nine hundred cases of poisoning associated with occupational exposure to pesticides are
reported in California annually, but according to Dr.
Hayes it is clear that many of these were so mild that
they might not have been reported if they had not been
covered by workmen's compensation.[11]

One of the leading experts on the diagnosis and
treatment of pesticide poisoning is Mitchell R. Zavon
of the University of Cincinnati College of Medicine. Dr.
Zavon emphasizes that symptoms of poisoning are well
defined and are usually clearly associated with the cause.

"Exposure to an insecticide such as parathion does not cause illness a week after that one-time exposure nor does exposure to parathion result in just any type of illness," he says. "Illness resulting from exposure to chemicals, and pesticides are usually chemicals, results in a disease pattern specific for that particular chemical. There are variants in response to the chemical but the variations are comparatively narrow." [12]

A recent development now makes it seem likely that a way will soon be found to make pesticides less toxic to both man and animals. Small amounts of drugs like phenobarbital cause the liver to act to detoxify pesticides like DDT and chlordane, changing them into substances that are quickly removed from the body, a panel of scientists told the January, 1966, meeting of the American Chemical Society. Though the effect also causes reduced fertility, the chemists believe that the discovery will lead to much greater safety with pesticides, the January 20, 1966, issue of the *New York Times* reported.

At present the greatest hazard from pest poisons, it should be pointed out, faces the man who applies them. Though safety results from proper methods of application, accidents are always possible. Agriculture is one of the nation's most hazardous occupations, and not as a result of pesticides. Most of the accidents involve tractors and other machinery. But of pesticides, some of the non-persistent types are more hazardous to handle than the persistent ones. Parathion, for instance, can be absorbed through the skin and is difficult to wash off. An insecticide that decays rapidly may also have to be applied several times a season to combat different pests with different life cycles, or different generations of the same pest, while one application of a persistent one may serve for a whole year. As Dr. Darby said at the Ribicoff hearings:

§

> [F]or man the greatest known hazard from pesticides is the operational one. Persistent pesticides may pose a greater hazard to some wildlife species than do the nonpersistent ones, but if persistent pesticides are arbitrarily eliminated from man's armamentarium against disease and hunger we might well be buying some hoped-for reduction in hazard to wildlife at the cost of a known increase in acute hazard to man.[13]

Now we move from the area of acute effects of pesticides, where facts are known or knowable and the picture is relatively clear, to a dim, fuzzy world of if, maybe, or perhaps. This is where those opposed to the use of pesticides thrive. It could be the presence of pesticides in the environment has chronic effects we do not even know about, they say. Who knows but what they account for all the maladies whose causes are not known. Could it be that pesticides cause cancer, leukemia, liver disease, loss of mental power, genetic damage, that tired, run-down feeling? "Their presence," says Miss Rachel Carson, "is no less ominous because it is formless and obscure, no less frightening because it is simply impossible to predict the effects of lifetime exposure to chemical and physical agents that are not part of the biological experience of man." [14]

One feels helpless to deal with this kind of attack. The known facts can be listed and explained. The safeguards of law can be demonstrated and the lack of evidence of harm can be cited. But this somehow seems inadequate. What if, after all, beyond all knowledge and reason, pesticides *are* preparing to destroy us all? We might never have a chance to admit we were wrong.

Do we therefore keep all the windows shut and eat only bread from wheat grown in unsprayed fields of far-off Afghanistan? This attitude was once captured in a few lines in the *New England Journal of Medicine:*

> So let your life be ordered
> By each documented fact
> And die of malnutrition
> But with arteries intact.

One must remember that there is no such thing as absolute safety. It is impossible to prove that any substance will under no circumstances injure anybody anywhere. But one can say, after a careful scrutiny of all known factors, that a given substance in given quantities will *probably* not hurt anyone. And the more facts on hand, the greater the confidence with which a conclusion can be drawn. So let us examine the ifs, maybes, and perhapses—and the facts, and what responsible scientists and other experts say about them.

One of medicine's most outspoken critics of pesticides is Irma West of the Bureau of Occupational Health, California Department of Public Health. At the 1964 American Medical Association Congress on Environmental Health Problems she presented a paper in which she charged that, "unforeseen, irrevocable, and undesirable side effects have arisen on a sizable scale from the use of pesticides." If anyone knows of hidden, late-emerging effects she presumably does, as the physician primarily responsible for California's occupational health program dealing with pesticides and other agricultural chemicals. But Dr. West offered no evidence of ill effects to man except for accidental cases of clear-cut poisoning. Her other evidence included the alleged endrin poisoning of fish in the Mississippi River and the implication that the pesticide reached the river from farmland.[15] As is shown in Chapter 9, this just isn't so.

Other participants in the same conference took pains to contradict any suggestion that pesticide residues endanger the general population. Robert Blackwell Smith, Jr., president of the Medical College of Virginia, declared: "I know of no evidence that the presence in the human diet of pesticide residues at or below the tolerance levels, set by law on the basis of animal data, has had any adverse effect on the health of our citizens." Dr. Zavon agreed:

§

> We have no evidence at present that the extremely small amounts of certain pesticides found in our food or in our general environment cause us any harm. . . . Allegations that pesticides may cause subtle, ill-defined effects cannot be refuted because we do not know what to refute.

In a summary of the proceedings, Raymond L. White of the AMA's Division of Environmental Medicine and Medical Services said:

§

There are uncertainties in the use of pesticides, but the overt hazards are no greater today than a decade ago and are probably far outweighed by the advantages of food production and the potential control of some 27 diseases which affect mankind.[16]

One fact no expert disputes is that small amounts of DDT and probably other pesticides are being stored in most people's tissues. Scientists first reported this in 1951, and every new study since then has confirmed the finding.

However, the average storage level of DDT and the less toxic compounds formed from it in the body, such as DDE, has remained almost constant since first measured. The level is around 10 or 12 parts per million. One recent research project found small amounts of lindane and dieldrin but no other pesticide.[17]

These findings tend to confirm a conclusion reached by Dr. Hayes in 1958 that was questioned in *Silent Spring*. Miss Carson, while not flatly disagreeing with this conclusion, cited other reports that DDT tended to accumulate in the tissues in larger and larger amounts, presumably representing a constantly increasing threat to health. Dr. Hayes's studies indicated, on the other hand, that though DDT storage increased with higher rates of intake, eventually an equilibrium was reached, with the storage level constant and the amount excreted the same as the amount consumed.[18]

This conclusion has been drawn from a more recent study along similar lines by William F. Durham of the Communicable Disease Center station in Wenatchee,

Washington. As in numbers of other tests, Dr. Durham's experiment involved long-term feeding of measured amounts of DDT to human volunteers. The amounts were 3.5 mg and 35 mg per man each day. Though these are only about 0.1 thousandth of an ounce and 1 thousandth of an ounce respectively, they represent 20 times and 200 times the amount consumed by the average person in a day. The dosage was continued for 21 months and the subjects were kept under observation for 37 more months. Dr. Durham found again that the amount of DDT stored depended directly on the amount consumed, that the amount excreted eventually came into balance with the amount taken in, and that after the dosage stopped the amount excreted tapered off slowly —meaning, one would conclude, that the storage level was dropping. As in other feeding experiments with DDT, no ill effects were reported by or observed in the subjects.[19]

One authority, incidentally, states that most reports of DDT poisoning have proved to be due to the solvent, frequently kerosene.[20]

Another study at the Communicable Disease Center in Wenatchee analyzed 177 food items found in restaurant and home meals for content of DDT and DDE. The conclusion was that dietary exposure to DDT has not increased in the ten previous years and may have decreased.[21]

A recent study involving another insecticide, methoxychlor, was similar to the DDT feeding test. A group at the Albany (New York) Medical College of Union University gave human volunteers daily doses of the chemical at 200 times the maximum permissible limit for foods. Detailed examinations discovered no harmful effects.[22]

The climate of Phoenix, Arizona, attracts asthma sufferers from all over the country. Aerial treatment of Arizona cotton and other crops with parathion and similar organic compounds produced a flood of complaints from people who lived near the fields. The pesticides were aggravating their condition or otherwise poisoning them, they asserted.

A careful study was undertaken, using asthmatic and nonasthmatic control groups and also observing nonasthmatic crop dusters and others exposed in their jobs. No sign of poisoning was detected in the people who lived near the fields, and the researchers concluded that their actual exposure was extremely small. The incidence of these people's asthma was also quite similar to that of the asthmatic control group, though the researchers did not rule out some effect of the pesticide applications on their asthma because the attacks were closely linked in time to their exposure to insecticides.[23]

Still another study focused on 15 people who had worked in a chlordane plant from one to fifteen years. Under constant but very small exposure to the insecticide, they showed no evidence of injury to any of their body organs. Since their exposure was greater than could be expected for users of the chemical, the investigators concluded that it presented little if any hazard when properly employed.[24]

The description of such studies could be extended almost indefinitely, with the same result. Descriptions of

ill effects from pesticides almost invariably disclose some
violation of safety practices or another departure from
recommended use. In the case of the asthma sufferers,
the effect seems to have been little different from what
might be expected from exposure to pollen or dust.

Are pesticides a cause of human cancer? Miss Carson devoted a chapter of *Silent Spring* to an attempt to
suggest that they are. She quoted an American Cancer
Society estimate that 45 million Americans now living
will eventually develop cancer—apparently the source
for her chapter title, "One in Every Four," since the
death rate she mentions is 15 per cent, or a little more
than one in every seven.[25] The suggestion is a grave one.
What is the answer?

The answer is, some are carcinogenic, or cancer-
causing, and some are not. However, no residues of those
that are carcinogenic are permitted on foods under the
"no-tolerance" provision of the law. The vigilance of
the Food and Drug Administration in enforcing this
provision for one chemical, aminotriazole, on cranberries is well remembered and is summarized in Chapter
9. Both manufacturers and the FDA are keenly alert to
the possibility that any material may be carcinogenic,
and they require intensive research in this area. Farmers
are also extremely careful, for no one wants his crop
seized.

Dr. Hayes, on the basis of personal research and
a thorough knowledge of the field, said in a statement
before the Ribicoff hearings that toxicologists are con-

stantly alert to the possibility that a chemical will affect someone in a way that was previously unknown or will aggravate another kind of disease, as prolonged inhalation of granite dust promotes tuberculosis. They also keep watch on diseases of unknown cause and diseases that are becoming more widespread, he said. When someone suggested that DDT might cause polio, he recalled, the possibility was considered and the lack of evidence was noted; when the polio vaccines were developed, such claims subsided.

"No matter what the source of suspicion, it is the responsibility of professional toxicologists to explore each possibility," Dr. Hayes said. "This is nothing new, and the search will continue indefinitely.

"However, it is important to realize that there is no conclusive evidence that pesticides, old or new, are a cause of any disease except poisoning."

This statement was based not only on observations of the whole population but on careful studies of workers exposed to pesticides in their jobs, such as workers in chemical plants and people who handle spraying equipment, and on studies of people who have agreed to take known doses and undergo tests, such as those already described. If cancer were to develop in anyone because of pesticide exposure it should develop in these people first. Cancer of the bladder, for instance, has been traced to certain dyes on the basis of studies of workers exposed to them. No such findings have been discovered with pesticides.

"[S]ome doubt is associated at once with any case

alleged to result from exposure that is trivial in comparison with what people ordinarily withstand without inconvenience," Dr. Hayes commented.[26]

Other studies have attempted to detect any increase in cancer among all the people living in areas where pesticides have come to be heavily used. One of these studies was made in the Mississippi Delta, part of which lies in my own Congressional district. It noted that during the four years following the introduction of modern pesticides to the area, the incidence of cancer declined, while in Mississippi as a whole it increased. In fact, the only malady that increased in the Delta to any degree was heart disease, and this increase was in line with the experience of the rest of the state, including areas where pesticides are used very little.[27]

What is the evidence about the most widely distributed pesticide, DDT? It has sometimes been accused of being carcinogenic because in one of the early studies, nodules regarded as adenomas (benign tumors) or low-grade cell carcinomas (minor malignancies) were detected in rats after 18 months of dosage. This effect has not been noted in other test animals, possibly because more recent studies have used a purer form of DDT. One study found no essential difference between DDT storage in persons who died of cancer and persons who died of other diseases. Another early experiment indicated that DDT had some curative action on cancer, but the effect was not considered strong enough to be useful. But a close relative, DDD, has been used in treatment of tumors of the adrenal cortex.[28] Tumors similar to those produced in the rats can also develop from overfeeding them.[29]

Arsenic has long been suspected of being carcinogenic on the basis of studies of diseases in the population, but some extensive studies of exposed workers have failed to verify the suspicion. No evidence that arsenic can create tumors in animals has been published, and one experiment attempting to prove this did not. Someone has pointed out that the increase in lung cancer in the United States paralleled an increase in the use of arsenical pesticides on tobacco, but another researcher noted that in Turkey, where very little arsenic is used in tobacco fields, there is also a high incidence of lung cancer among cigarette smokers. In any case, it is almost impossible not to eat arsenic, since it is a natural component of many foods, as Dr. Darby pointed out, and is present in milk at levels of about 0.3 to 0.5 parts per million on a dry-weight basis.[30]

Aramite, a mite-killer, passed its cancer test in rats but later was shown to cause tumors in dogs fed large amounts in their diets. It is now in use on a zero-tolerance basis. Aminotriazole, the chemical involved in the cranberry scare, reduces the activity and enlarges the thyroid of rats. Some researchers regard this as cancerous and others, noting that normal function is restored when the herbicide is withdrawn from the diet, do not. Nevertheless, no residue is permitted on any food. Aldrin and dieldrin produce liver tumors in mice, but since the tumors are benign the pesticides are not regarded as carcinogenic. Feeding tests with mice, rats, and dogs of the carbamate IPC and its relative, CIPC, showed no tendency to produce cancer, but when given to mice whose skins were daubed at the same time with croton oil, which raises blisters, a number of tumors were observed on those skin areas. Other carbamates have been shown to be carcinogenic.[31]

This, in brief, is a description of the results of studies of pesticides as cancer-causing agents. As one can see there is no little research in the area, and the known or even suspected carcinogens are strictly controlled. On what, then, do the proponents of the cancer theory base their charges?

The two men on whom Rachel Carson rests her case are Wilhelm C. Hueper, chief of the Environmental Cancer Section of the National Cancer Institute in Washington, and Malcolm M. Hargarves, professor of medicine at the Mayo Foundation, associated with the Mayo Clinic in Rochester, Minnesota. Both men appeared before the Ribicoff inquiry.

In his testimony, Dr. Hueper made a number of statements that later were shown to be mistakes—for instance, that sodium arsenite is sold as a weed-killer for lawns (it is not), that arsenical pesticides are widely used on fruit (the use has almost disappeared), that processors dip apples in liquid paraffin to seal in the water and incidentally the insecticide (apples do a fine job of supplying their own wax). In attacking pesticides, he said:

§

The evidence on hand is sufficiently substantial for supporting the view that the rapidly growing exposure of the general population to pesticides of diverse chemical nature, of diverse biologic activity, and from multiple sources—occupation, foodstuffs, drinking water, general air, clothes, home environment, and so forth—should arouse concern and apprehension. . . .[32]

His response to questions from Senator James B. Pearson of Kansas went like this:

§

SENATOR PEARSON. . . . Doctor, I understand you don't give slide rule answers to questions in this field, but on the basis of this statement, is the point you have developed that chemical compounds used in pesticides in controlled experiments have produced cancer?

DR. HUEPER. That is right.

SENATOR PEARSON. And that these same chemical compounds used in pesticides are now being used in a commercial sense for foodstuffs and feed grains and so forth?

DR. HUEPER. That is right.

SENATOR PEARSON. Do you have evidence from your own research or experimentation that the residues in these feed grains and so forth are sufficient to produce cancer?

DR. HUEPER. That evidence is not available. . . .[33]

Dr. Hargraves was concerned with a much wider range of chemicals than just pesticides, particularly those containing benzene, a widely used solvent and a constituent of gasoline. Benzene, or benzol, he said, is the principal cause, in genetically susceptible people, of blood disorders, including leukemia.

§

I feel that I can state an axiom as well as theorems, which is that although not all persons with a significant history of exposure will become victims of leukemia or lymphoma, all persons with lymphoma or leukemia seem to have a significant history of the exposure in question. . . . I think that it becomes obvious from these statements that they are based upon observation and deduction and lack the unassailable proof which supports other accepted biological theories.[34]

How, then, can it be an axiom, which means a self-evident truth? And who in America is not exposed to gasoline and paint?

For an answer to Dr. Hargraves we need only turn again to the statement of Dr. Hayes—that despite the watchfulness and experiments of experts, paying particular attention to occupationally exposed groups, "There is no conclusive evidence that pesticides, old or new, are a cause of any disease except poisoning."

Under the committee's questioning, Dr. Hayes added that he and other authorities agreed that "at least 95 per cent of cancer, as it now exists, is indistinguishable from cancer that occurred a generation or two ago, and that it is not environmentally caused in the sense of any new element in the environment.

"Now, whether it is caused by something that existed in the environment of our grandparents is quite another matter," he said. "But it is not caused by anything that is new in our environment."

Dr. Hayes said his laboratory had conducted studies of cancer and had published at least two papers on the effect of DDT and other pesticides on the liver. But the only time he had a positive result the cause was not the chemical under study. He continued:

§

We can synthetically produce leukemia in rats by a special purified diet, which we had wished to use for certain experimental reasons. The leukemia was transmissible from rat to rat, and we have sent rats up to NIH [National Institutes of Health] for further study to determine whether a virus is responsible for it.

In some instances the cause of cancer in animals has been proved to be certain chemicals. In other instances it has been proved just as positively that cancer was caused by viruses. The relation between these is still largely unexplored, but is being investigated.

There are experts in the cancer field who feel that it is just a matter of time and hard work until cancer in people, as it occurs in the general population, and as it has occurred as a serious disease of man as long as we have known about it, will be traced to a virus infection.[35]

One more witness before the Ribicoff hearings might be cited to answer some of the charges against pesticides. He is Charles Henri Hine, associate clinical professor of Preventive [Occupational] Medicine and Toxicology at the University of California School of Medicine.

On Dr. Hargraves' theory that pesticides cause blood disorders, Dr. Hine said:

§

I have to disagree with my colleague, Dr. Hargraves. I do not think, in most instances, there is a good cause-and-effect relationship with the blood dyscrasias [disorders]. I think this is relatively rare with the insecticides.

Here is what Dr. Hine said of the suggestion that pesticides are responsible for influenza-like states referred to as virus X:

§

These situations are not considered to be related by the great majority of physicians.

To the suggestion that pesticides may cause mental disorders; he replied:

§

In my experience I have seen persons who, having suffered from a severe intoxication [poisoning], manifest increased anxiety and signs of neuroses; but the occurrence of these signs and symptoms in this group of persons is no different from that observed in others who have had significant threats to their body and psyche and have subsequently responded with a post-traumatic neurosis.

Of the suggestion that pesticides are responsible for cases of general malaise, a feeling of decreased efficiency, general weakness, and tiredness, he replied:

§

The ubiquity of these symptoms among the population in general and the lack of relation to any specific environmental exposure has in my opinion negated any relationship.

To the suggestion that pesticides aggravate underlying disease he states:

§

There is no reasonable medical evidence which would substantiate this conclusion.

On the suggestion that pesticides affect reproduction and cause mutations, he commented:

§

I know of no evidence at the present time which would suggest there is any risk of this nature. Experiments on animals have indicated that high concentrations of the materials may produce a decreased number of surviving young. However, the majority of tests have indicated that there is no effect in this direction at concentrations which are likely to be met by man.[36]

On one point experts and would-be experts of every persuasion agree—there is a great need for more research. This is normal; it would be surprising if someone said there were no need for more research. The history of science shows that the process of finding the answers to questions always raises new questions that need to be answered. So under the impetus of *Silent Spring*, the report of the President's Science Advisory Committee, and the Ribicoff hearings, Congress has provided funds for greatly expanded research into the effects of pesticides. This research is under way. Many reports have yet to be published, but there is no indication at this writing that any results will be cause for alarm.

One type of study that was widely urged, for instance, was the "community study" to measure the average exposure to pesticides from people's total environment, not just their food supply. The Public Health Service began ten such studies in 1964, and Department of Agriculture monitoring operations are cooperating with them. Information on the presence of pesticides and the level of residues in people's bodies will be used to estimate the hazard from pesticide exposure. Many other new research projects are examining the effects of pesticides on animals and man. The result is sure to sharpen our knowledge of pesticides and how to use them safely. In the meantime, the knowledge and techniques we have seem quite adequate to protect the health of the nation's citizens.

One of the most effective voices in quieting the fears aroused by vague charges against pesticides has

been that of Frederick J. Stare, professor and chairman
of the Department of Nutrition, School of Public Health,
Harvard University. A recent article by Dr. Stare, whose
newspaper column is widely read, is worth reproducing
in full:

§

The current hysteria about agricultural chemicals has
seeped in under the doorsills of American homes.

A woman recently said to me, "I feel like Lucretia Borgia
every time I put dinner on the table. Am I poisoning my
family?"

That concerned woman, interested primarily in the health
and well-being of her family, deserves to have an end put to
her confusion about agricultural chemicals, particularly pesticides. Her bafflement stems not from stupidity, but from the
claims and counter-claims of self-appointed experts who usually
don't know what they're talking about.

They are usually extrapolating to man some findings on
birds, bees or fish, or the unfortunate result of some child inhal-
ing or swallowing large quantities of some pesticide. Such findings just don't extend to the use of agricultural chemicals in
growing, protecting or preserving of foods.

Let's set aside all arguments about how or why the current
controversy started and concentrate instead on letting facts speak
for themselves.

One irrefutable fact the critics of pesticides have been unable to answer is this true statement: there is not one medically
documented instance of ill health in man, not to mention death,
that can be attributed to the proper use of pesticides, or even
to their improper use as far as ill health from residues on foods.

If anyone can bring forward any evidence to refute that,
there are many agencies, including the Food and Drug Administration, the Public Health Service and the Food Protection
Committee of the Food and Nutrition Board, that would welcome an opportunity to investigate the case.

In spite of this lack of evidence, many people now have the
impression that pesticides contaminate our food supply and are
harmful, probably lethal. This gap between fact and fancy must
be closed or we will do ourselves great harm by allowing disease
and famine to rule the earth.

Are pesticides poison? Of course, that's why they work.
They are poison to the insects, worms, rats, weeds and other
pests against which they are directed. Because of strictly en-

forced regulations and tolerance levels, however, the hazard to man from pesticide residues on foods is almost nonexistent. They are dangerous if you handle them carelessly or leave them around where small fry may "play house" with them.

You can have full confidence in our foods. They are not full of poisons as some food faddists would have you believe. They are nutritious and the quality is much better than it was a generation ago.

Eat and enjoy them.[37]

NOTES TO CHAPTER 5

1. *New York Times*, March 12, p. 23, March 13, p. 22, 1962.
2. *Interagency Coordination in Environmental Hazards (Pesticides)*, hearings before the Subcommittee on Reorganization and International Organizations of the Committee on Government Operations, U.S. Senate, 88th Congress, 1st Session (Washington: Government Printing Office, 1964), Part III, pp. 652–653.
3. Wayland J. Hayes, Jr., "Pharmacology and Toxicology of DDT," in Paul Müller (*Ed.*), *DDT: The Insecticide Dichlorodiphenyltrichloroethane and Its Significance* (Basel and Stuttgart: Birkhäuser Verlag, 1959), II, pp. 120–136.
4. *Interagency Coordination*, Part II, pp. 407-408.
5. Auto deaths: 1965 figure from estimate by the Division of Accident Prevention, U.S. Public Health Service, based on 10% sample of traffic deaths through October, 1965; to be published. Falls: Vital Statistics of the United States, 1964, to be published by the U.S. Public Health Service. Deaths by fire arms: "Accident Facts for 1964," National Safety Council, Chicago, Illinois, 1965, p. 15. Accidental poisoning: Vital Statistics of the United States, 1964, to be published by the U.S. Public Health Service. See also, Louis A. McLean, "It Happened in America—Almost," speech presented to the Western Agricultural Chemicals Association at Portland, Ore., January 13, 1965, p. 5.
6. *Interagency Coordination*, Part II, pp. 443–445.
7. From the report of the Surveys and Investigations Staff of the House Committee on Appropriations, printed in *Department of Agriculture Appropriations for 1966*, hearings before a subcommittee of the Committee on Appropriations, House of Representatives, 88th Congress, 1st Session (Washington: Government Printing Office, 1965), Part I, p. 194.
8. Quoted in McLean, *op. cit.* p. 5.
9. *Department of Agriculture Appropriations for 1966*, Part I, p. 194.
10. Irma West, "Occupational Disease of Farm Workers," *Archives of Environmental Health*, IX (1964), p. 92.

11. Wayland J. Hayes, Jr., "Occurrence of Poisoning by Pesticides," *Archives of Environmental Health*, IX (1964), p. 622.
12. Mitchell R. Zavon, "Diagnosis and Treatment of Pesticide Poisoning," *Archives of Environmental Health*, IX (1964), pp. 616–617.
13. *Interagency Coordination*, Part III, p. 657.
14. Rachel Carson, *Silent Spring* (Boston: Houghton Mifflin Co., 1962), p. 188.
15. Irma West, "Pesticides as Contaminants," *Archives of Environmental Health*, IX (1964), p. 632.
16. *Archives of Environmental Health*, IX (1964), pp. 638, 616; *Science*, CXLV (1964), p. 730.
17. William S. Hoffman, William I. Fishbein, and Morten B. Andelman, "Pesticide Storage in Human Fat Tissue," *Journal of the American Medical Association*, Vol. 188, No. 9 (June, 1964), p. 819.
18. Carson, *op. cit.*, p. 22; Wayland J. Hayes, Jr., *et. al.*, "Storage of DDT and DDE in People With Different Degrees of Exposure to DDT," *AMA Archives of Industrial Health*, XVIII (1958), pp. 398–406.
19. William F. Durham, "Pesticide Exposure Levels in Man and Animals," *Archives of Environmental Health*, X (1965), p. 842.
20. Zavon, *op. cit.*, p. 617.
21. Reported in *Croplife*, May, 1965, p. 28.
22. *Ibid.*
23. Robert S. Ganelin, Cipriano Cueto, Jr., and G. Allen Mail, "Exposure to Parathion," *Journal of the American Medical Association*, Vol. 188, No. 9 (June, 1964), pp. 807–810.
24. J. V. White, Harry J. Isaacs, and William I, Fishbein, "Survey of Workers Exposed to Chlordane," *Industrial Medicine and Surgery*, XXXIII, No. 10 (October, 1964), pp. 726–727.
25. Carson, *op. cit.*, p. 221.
26. *Interagency Coordination*, Part II, p. 409.
27. Reported in William F. Durham, "Pesticide Residues in Foods in Relation to Human Health," in Francis A. Gunther (*Ed.*), *Residue Reviews* (Berlin, Gottingen, Heidelberg, and New York: Springer-Verlag, 1963), IV, p. 40.
28. *Ibid.*, pp. 45–46.
29. Statement by Charles Henri Hine in *Interagency Coordination*, Part II, p. 559.
30. Durham, *op. cit.*, pp. 41–42.
31. *Ibid.*, pp. 43–46.
32. *Interagency Coordination*, Part III, pp. 683–718.
33. *Ibid.*, p. 699.
34. *Ibid.*, Part II, p. 488.
35. *Ibid.*, p. 452.
36. *Ibid.*, pp. 558–559.
37. Frederick J. Stare, "Pesticides Not Injurious," *Evening Star* (Washington, D.C.), February 18, 1965.

CHAPTER 6

AND THE BIRDS
DO SING

MOST people have a special affection for the
creatures of the earth that exist independent of man.
People who live in urban residential areas try to attract
birds to their yards just because their songs and activities give pleasure. The 16 million people who hunt and
22 million who fish do so, surely, not from any hatred
of their game but from a kind of love for the outdoors
and the living things in it, including the prey they shoot
or hook. The rapidly soaring numbers of people who
observe birds and animals in the wild as a hobby and
who spend their vacations camping in our parks and
forests doubtless have similar feelings.

This special sentiment for untamed things appears
to be the reason that one of the principal issues in the
pesticide debate is the effect on wildlife. Because deep-
seated emotions are involved many people pay no attention to facts, or pick up only those facts that suit their
convictions. A single dead robin can be evidence of
criminal poisoning of the environment and an unfortunate miscalculation in a pest-eradication campaign
nine years ago is cited as evidence that use of insecticides should be sharply curtailed.

The fact is that the numbers of birds and many other forms of wildlife are mushrooming even faster than the human population and causing some very serious problems. Regardless of the result of a laboratory study of what heptachlor can do to a quail or a limited survey of a treated area, the evidence of the increase is plain in the rising number of hunters, the lengthening shooting seasons, and the increasing bag limits. It is clear in the size of the kill—9 million ducks, 5 million pheasants, 2 million deer and elk (deer in many areas are so numerous that they are threatening to overgraze their feeding grounds), and 14.5 million squirrels in 1963. It is clear from going to the woods and looking around as well as from the studies cited.

My experience in the Yazoo–Mississippi River Delta region has convinced me that the birds there have actually benefited from the use of pesticides because mites, rodents, and other enemies of birds have been destroyed and because the cultivation of more and more land for grain crops has provided the birds with a plentiful food supply. The Delta, as I have described, is intensively treated with pesticides to fight the boll weevil and other pests. On a recent dove-shooting trip there, my companions and I saw literally thousands of birds and hundreds of sportsmen. At the end of the day many thousands of birds were still flying everywhere.

A Mississippian who has special qualifications to speak on both pesticides and wildlife and combines this with unusual writing ability is Mabry I. Anderson. Mr. Anderson has run a large airplane spraying company operating in the Delta since 1946. He has also been an active conservationist for twenty-five years, serving as member and officer of state and national conservation groups and contributing numerous articles to outdoor magazines. His indignation at the misinformation in circulation concerning the two fields to which he has devoted his life found an outlet in 1964 in an article titled "The Case FOR Pesticides." Here is what he said on the question of wildlife population:

§

In 1946, when pesticide use became big business, wildlife populations in the delta, and all over Mississippi, were at relatively low levels. Deer were legal in only a few counties; even as late as 1953 the legal kill of bucks was only 2,300. However, population increases began about 1946, and they skyrocketed the kill at a rate of more than 20 percent increase each year. In 1962 the legal kill had risen to 14,687; the 1963 kill is estimated to be more than 18,000.

Wild turkey were at such a low ebb in 1946 that a completely closed season was ordered for 1947 and 1948. In 1948, however, populations began to climb steadily. Today counties with open turkey seasons have almost doubled, and in the delta, where pesticide use is heaviest, open seasons have almost trebled, with the bag limit raised from one to three birds a year. Most upland game has followed the same pattern, wherever suitable habitat existed. Doves, quail, rabbits, and squirrels were never more abundant than now and fishing is unsurpassed.

The article quoted James Russell of Jonestown, who owns several thousand acres that have been in his family since before the Civil War:

§

"The thing that most conservationists and nature lovers seem to forget," he says, "is that most modern cultural practices are the best friend wildlife has, and I am including pesticide use. On our land, a successful insect-control program helps us produce yields that are double or even treble what they used to be. Consequently we've been able to cut back our cotton acreage

drastically. Twenty-five years ago we planted almost every acre
in cotton, and this left nothing much for quail and doves. Today
we plant only about a third of the land in cotton, and the rest
goes to soybeans, oats, wheat, and the soil-conservation programs
that produce food and cover for game.

"Now there is more game on our land than ever before, including deer, a species that disappeared in the thirties. In addition, we've dammed up a bayou for irrigation purposes, drilled
a deep well, and created a very good duck lake as a byproduct.
I don't like the trend that this criticism is taking, and if it keeps
up I'm afraid that farmer-sportsman relationships are going to
suffer." [1]

Is the Delta an isolated case, attributable to some
special, unknown factor? Not at all. Rather this is a fair
description of the general picture in the country, as put
together in a months-long, nationwide survey conducted
in 1963 by the magazine *Sports Illustrated*. In what it
called a series of "startling counterrevelations," the
magazine asserted:

Wildlife populations all over the nation are bigger
and healthier than ever, not in spite of pesticides, but in
many cases because of them.

A great many pesticide disasters and portents of
disaster, reported in newspapers and elsewhere, turned
out to be exaggerations, in one case amounting to two
dead pheasants.

The wildlife poisonings that did occur were invariably the result of misuse or negligence, not the inevitable
result of prescribed application.

In the 1963 hunting season, the magazine reported,
17 big-game and 24 small-game species were open, more
than in years. No state had curtailed its hunting season
because of losses caused by pesticides, and no state

could point to an overall drop in game that could be
laid to pesticides. In some states the seasons had just
been made longer and more liberal.

The survey continued:

§

    In Texas, where recent rumblings of pesticide-poisoned
quail have been heard, game wardens report that "hunters have
looked for and found more birds than last year," and wildlife
officials are talking about extending the season. Elsewhere, the
wild turkey, once nearly extinct and closed to hunting over
much of its original range in the early '40's when pesticides
came into widespread use, can be hunted today in 26 states.
Ruffed grouse are peaking in much of their range. New population explosions are reported among Midwestern rabbits. Louisiana's deer herds are growing so fast in prime cotton country,
where heavy spraying occurs, that the chief problem is finding
enough hunters to harvest them. And Washington game protec-
tors are complaining about deer increases that keep the wardens
up nights chasing the animals away from the farmers' well-
sprayed fruit trees.

The article quotes Dr. Justin Leonard of the Michigan Department of Conservation on the effect of pesticide application: "Frankly, I don't think it makes too
much difference. We lose more ducks to botulism than
to pesticides." [2]

Mr. Wheeler Johnson, Outdoor Editor of *The
Washington Star*, commenting on the "Blizzard of '66"
in the February 13, 1966, edition of that paper, said
that animal life had weathered the storm remarkably
well. He quoted Ralph Biteley, Maryland's Chief of
Wildlife Management, who had made aerial surveys:

§

    About the only loss of life I've noticed has been a few doves
and every winter you find them dead in the fields. They can't

stand cold, apparently, but this is to be expected. The mortality rate for doves runs from 60 to 80 percent every year, which is normal for birds and animals that have a high birth rate.

Another evidence of the greater abundance of birds is the annual bird count of the National Audubon Society, reported each year in *Audubon Field Notes,* which is a quick, accurate source of information on population trends, and a very good inventory of our December bird life. In 1940 the survey counted 2 million birds. In 1961 there were four times as many people taking part, but the sample census showed 37.8 million birds, almost 19 times the 1940 figure.[3]

Widespread agricultural use of pesticides also seems to have done nothing to reduce the population of bird pests. Vast flocks of blackbirds steal from feed lots and grainfields of the Southeast. Forty million of these birds are said to frequent one roost in Arkansas. The Bureau of Sport Fisheries and Wildlife of the Fish and Wildlife Service told the House Committee on Appropriations in 1964 that 227 starling-blackbird roosts had been located the winter before that contained an estimated 204 million birds and that 80 of the roosts contained a million or more birds each. Most, it said, were in the Arkansas-Mississippi rice-growing region, the area of perhaps the heaviest use of pesticides in the nation. The Bureau was requesting $1,059,000 to finance research on this problem and the related ones of animal damage.[4]

Supporting this request, the Bureau explained in a statement (emphasis supplied):

§

Concentrations of birds cause a variety of problems in the United States—from a noise and filth nuisance in residential and business districts; to excessive damage on a host of truck, field and orchard crops; to hazards at and around airports and along the airways. No one can say just how much damage in terms of dollars birds do. However, a recent (1963) incomplete survey by the American Farm Bureau Federation put the annual loss to agriculture at about $28 million.

Geographically, the bird problem of immediate concern to the Bureau of Sport Fisheries and Wildlife is widespread, extending from the Atlantic coast to Midway Island and from the northernmost reaches of small grain farming in Canada, deep into the cultivated lands of Mexico. While blackbirds and starlings are the major culprits, a large number of species are involved *including some of our treasured song and game birds.*[5]

The records of another agency, the Federal Aviation Agency, indicate that, since 1956, seven major commercial airline accidents, involving 79 fatalities, have been caused by birds striking the aircraft. Since 1959, 156 collisions with birds have been reported by commercial aircraft, from which no accident resulted.

In 1963, Lansing A. Parker, Assistant Director, Bureau of Sport Fisheries and Wildlife, testified: "Last year [1962], for example, we made some studies . . . to determine the source of the birds that were causing the trouble. In the middle of the winter there were heavy concentrations running as high as four to six million birds in a single roost."

The Bureau of Sport Fisheries and Wildlife also happens to be one of the principal agencies investigating the effects of pesticides on wildlife. One of its major efforts over the past decade has been to analyze the effect of the fire-ant eradication program in the Southeast, which involved use of heptachlor over wide areas. Results of this study were still being published in a professional journal in 1965. So far they report that the quail population was sharply cut in the area treated with heptachlor at the rate of 2 pounds per acre and remained below previous levels for several years.[6]

It may be, as its critics charge, that the fire-ant program was conceived and put into execution with too little awareness of what its effects might be. Here is how Secretary of Agriculture Orville L. Freeman explained it to the Senate subcommittee investigating pesticides under Senator Abraham Ribicoff:

§

> The initial treatment consisted of a single application of 2 pounds of heptachlor per acre. This treatment effectively killed fire ants but it also killed some desirable fish and wildlife. By tightening specifications and working with insecticide producers to obtain more uniform formulations, we were able to reduce the dosage, space out its application, and do the job about as well with virtually no hazard to wildlife.
>
> The big breakthrough came in 1961, however, with the development by industry of an insecticide called Mirex. On the background of 10 years' work, our scientists came up with a new combination: Mirex as the killer, soybean oil as an attractant, and ground corncob grits for a carrier. Less than one-seventh of an ounce of Mirex in 5 pounds of bait evenly distributed over each acre of infested land now effectively controls fire ants. It has no harmful effect on people, domestic animals, fish, wildlife, or even bees, and it leaves no residue in milk, meat, or crops.[7]

Let it also be said that the evidence is by no means clear-cut that even the heptachlor phase of the fire-ant program always killed wildlife. A Florida study, for instance, failed to discover any significant effect on wildlife with heptachlor applied at the rate of 1.25 pounds per acre.[8] In terms of field populations, surely the most significant evidence is that conservation officials have felt game numbers to be high enough to increase limits in the very areas treated for the fire ant. Perhaps one reason for this is, as was pointed out in *Insects: The 1952 Yearbook of Agriculture,* that fire ants attack young quail in the nest. One study showed a 15 per cent loss of quail nests to the insect.[9]

Even in laboratory studies, it appears, there is much that is not known about how to interpret a finding that a certain level of a certain kind of insecticide in the diet does or does not kill certain birds. A report by William H. Stickel and others at the Patuxent Wildlife Research Center in Laurel, Maryland, says that the effect of DDT "amalgamated with the food"—earthworms—was more lethal to woodcocks than pure doses of DDT. But "birds in good condition could scarcely be killed by oral doses of DDT, even massive ones," the article said. "Some succumbed to smaller spaced serial doses, but only when these were accompanied by starvation rations." Heptachlor, too, affected underweight birds much more than normal ones.[10]

A California study of pheasants mentions that pesticides are likely to have a different effect on birds caught in the wild than on birds bred and raised in the pen. The study showed little or no effect from even lethal levels of DDT on egg fertility and survival of young and pointed out that "annual mortality rates as high as 73 per cent are considered normal for stable pheasant populations in the wild." Pesticides are often accused of reducing the fertility of wild birds.[11]

It has been found that fish in inland lakes in Sunflower County, Mississippi, and other areas where pesticides are extensively used have stored 40 times as much pesticide in their fat as the fish that supposedly were killed by pesticides in the Mississippi River in 1963. Yet these lake fish were plump and lively. Studies of fish at Mississippi State University show that fish over several generations develop a genetic resistance to pesticides, just as insects do.[12]

Does spraying lakes and marshes for mosquito control always harm fish and wildlife? Many people seem to think so, but there are ways to do it without harm. According to Neely Turner of the Connecticut Agricultural Experiment Station, New Haven, it has been shown repeatedly that insecticides can be used on water safely by using proper materials at proper dosages at the right time. In Connecticut, he said, the recommended application is 0.2 pounds of DDT per acre for single treatments and 0.1 pounds per acre for repeated treatments, with malathion at 0.2 pounds per acre an alternative.

Mr. Turner also provides one of the most sensible discussions on record of the use of DDT to combat Dutch elm disease. He notes that in the Midwest, robins have been killed by feeding on poisonous worms under trees sprayed with DDT. In Connecticut there has been one serious case of robin poisoning. This occurred when homeowners applied DDT to their lawns to control the

Japanese beetle; a short, hard rain washed the chemical into puddles; and robins drank the water. But there is no record of robin deaths in the state from spraying for Dutch elm disease. He continued:

§

> We could conclude that the deaths had been unnoticed, or that the spray in Connecticut did not kill robins. Dr. C. C. Doane of our department collected earthworms from soil under trees in two parks where DDT spraying had been done for years. In one analysis considerable DDT was found but in the other there was little DDT. A study of the spray practices revealed other differences. In Illinois, "several" applications were made to the foliage to control pests other than the elm bark beetle [the vector of Dutch elm disease]. In Connecticut only one spray was applied to foliage, and in some places arsenate of lead was used instead of DDT. In Illinois, the campus of many acres had hundreds of elm trees, and a very large nesting area was treated. In Connecticut, the largest park had only dozens of elm trees and a small nesting area. Furthermore, most of the elms treated in Connecticut were street trees, and in few cases were there any earthworms.
>
> Regardless of these differences, it is obvious that continued treatment of elms with DDT, and possibly continued treatment of turf for Japanese beetles, may contaminate earthworms, and at some future date sufficiently so to kill birds feeding on the worms. Thus the only effective way of combating Dutch elm disease is somewhat hazardous to birds. Someone may have to decide whether our parks have elms or robins. At the present time, the record indicates that the hazard of an elm dying from Dutch elm disease is greater than of a robin being killed by sprays that protect the elms. This does not mean that people must spray for the disease, but that they can still do so without certain death of birds.[13]

A report issued by the National Academy of Sciences—National Research Council in 1963 called for several different lines of research. Among the goals it urged were better application methods, materials that affect pests as much as present pesticides but other life less, knowledge of what happens to pesticides after application, and nonchemical control methods. These are all worthwhile aims, and research is already underway on all of them.

But let it not be forgotten that the first sentence of the report said: "Pest control to protect human health, food, fiber, forest and other biological resources is essential by whatever means necessary." [14]

NOTES TO CHAPTER 6

1. Mabry I. Anderson, "The Case FOR Pesticides," *Field & Stream*, LXIX, No. 5 (September, 1964), pp. 12–16, 32.
2. Virginia Kraft, "The Life-Giving Spray," *Sports Illustrated*, XIX, No. 21 (Nov. 18, 1963), pp. 22–25, 72–73.
3. "Noisy Springs," *The Oregonian* (Portland, Oregon) July 20, 1964.
4. *Department of the Interior and Related Agencies Appropriations for 1965*, hearings before a subcommittee of the Committee on Appropriations, House of Representatives, 88th Congress, 1st Session (Washington: Government Printing Office, 1964), pp. 324–325.
5. From *Hearings on the Department of the Interior Appropriations for 1965*, 88th Congress, 2d Session, pp. 313–315.
6. Walter Rosene, Jr., "Effects of Field Applications of Heptachlor on Bobwhite Quail and Other Wild Animals," *Journal of Wildlife Management*, XXIX (1965), pp. 554–580.
7. *Interagency Coordination in Environmental Hazards (Pesticides)*, hearings before the Subcommittee on Reorganization and International Organizations of the Committee on Government Operations, U.S. Senate, 88th Congress, 1st Session (Washington: Government Printing Office, 1964), Part I, p. 88.
8. From report of the Surveys and Investigations Staff of the House Committee on Appropriations, in *Department of Agriculture Appropriations for 1966*, hearings before a subcommittee of the Committee on Appropriations, House of Representatives, 89th Congress, 1st Session (Washington: Government Printing Office, 1965), Part I, p. 189.
9. J. P. Linduska and Arthur W. Lindquist, "Some Insect Pests of Wildlife," in U.S. Department of Agriculture, *Insects: The Yearbook of Agriculture, 1952* (Washington: Government Printing Office), p. 716.
10. William H. Stickel, *et al.*, "Body Condition and Response to Pesticides in Woodcocks," *Journal of Wildlife Management*, XXIX (1965), p. 155.
11. John A. Azevedo, Jr., Eldridge G. Hunt, and Leon A. Woods, Jr.,

"Physiological Effects of DDT on Pheasants," *California Fish and Game*, LI (1965), 276–293.

12. Abstracted in *Pesticide-Wildlife Studies by States, Provinces, and Universities: An Annotated List of Investigations Through 1964* (Fish and Wildlife Service Circular 224; Washington: Department of the Interior, 1965), p. 13.

13. Neely Turner, "Insecticides and Wildlife," in *Interagency Coordination*, Part I, Appendix IV, pp. 985–987.

14. Subcommittee on Research Needs, Committee on Pest Control and Wildlife Relationships, *Pest Control and Wildlife Relationships—Part III: Research Needs* (Publication 920-C; Washington: National Academy of Sciences–National Research Council, 1963), pp. 1, 26–27.

CHAPTER 7

Silent Spring

AND THE COMMITTEE
STAFF REPORT

F<small>EW</small> responsible people with knowledge of
the subject defend all the conclusions of Miss Rachel
Carson's *Silent Spring*. Even those who hail the work
for awakening the American people to the perils they
see in pesticides concede that some conclusions are
overdrawn or are based on inadequate evidence.

For instance, Dexter W. Masters, director of Consumers Union, which thought enough of *Silent Spring*
to bring out an edition of it, said in the foreword to that
edition:

§

Consumers Union cannot and does not endorse every point Miss
Carson makes. . . . [F]rom the wide range of her factual material she has proceeded to some conclusions with respect to
dangers to human health which seem to CU's medical advisers
extreme.[1]

Even when conceding the point, the typical advocate of *Silent Spring* shrugs and says Miss Carson's
methods were necessary to counter the threat to our

environment. Representative is this passage from an editorial in the Washington *Evening Star:*

§

> We do not doubt that some of the points made by Miss Carson in her book are debatable, largely because no one really knows all the facts. And the value of pesticides, properly used, should be obvious to anyone. It seems, however, that Miss Carson's detractors have missed the point of her book. What she wanted to do—and did do—was to jolt Americans out of their apathy toward the dangers of the indiscriminate use of pesticides. If she overdrew her conclusions, this was incidental to a message to her fellow countrymen that came through loud and clear. What will be remembered is that her book warned human beings of the dangers of becoming victims, if not directly then indirectly, of their own ingenuity.[2]

In other words, the end justifies the means. It would seem preferable to examine the issue dispassionately, correct any abuses that might be observed, and carefully balance any criticism of excess with the evidence easily obtainable on the benefits to man from the use of pesticides.

Perhaps the most impressive assessment of Miss Carson's work is provided by the report on pesticides of the Surveys and Investigations Staff of the House of Representatives' Committee on Appropriations. At the request of the Subcommittee on the Department of Agriculture, of which the author has the honor to be chairman, the staff undertook an objective and comprehensive study of the effects of the use of agricultural pesticides on public health. The staff of the Committee is headed by an experienced investigator. Once the purpose of the study was stated, the members of the com-

mittee had no voice in the staff's investigating procedures or in the choice of the experts it interviewed. The
intention was for the staff to present the committee with
a judicious summary of its findings, though the mass of
raw data is filed with the committee.

By a directive dated June 18, 1964, an inquiry was
requested into the following subjects:

§

(1) The extent to which the Departments of Agriculture,
Interior, and Health, Education and Welfare cooperate, collabo-
rate, and coordinate their activities so as to protect the public
health while minimizing any adverse effect on agricultural producers and processors and protecting the food supply for all
Americans with particular reference to—

(a) Regulations, procedures, and practices used in
approving and registering agricultural pesticides and other
control materials.

(b) Regulations, procedures, and practices followed in
formulating, reviewing, and agreeing upon changes in standards or tolerances previously used as basis for approval.

(c) Extent to which changes are reviewed and approved
by all appropriate Federal agencies prior to announcement
to the public.

(d) Extent to which such announced changes are based
on claims and documented evidence that the public health is
endangered.

(2) Regulations, if any, to control irresponsible actions,
statements, and criticisms of agricultural pesticides and the
instances of the effect on producers, processors, and consumers
during the past 10 years of such actions, statements, and criticisms, including information on:

(a) A chronological record of all instances similar to the
cranberry incident in 1959, the more recent condemnation
of milk in Maryland, and claims as to fishkills in the lower
Mississippi and Missouri Rivers.

(b) The basis for expressed or implied claims and
charges made public in each instance and the Federal agency
concerned.

(c) Efforts made to coordinate the actions of all Federal
agencies concerned with the problem.

(d) The ultimate costs to the producers, processors, consumers, and the Federal Government in each instance.

(e) The extent to which initial claims and charges were borne out by subsequent developments and findings.

(3) Information on current and long-range implications of programs and activities of the Department of Agriculture to minimize effects of the use of pesticides and to find alternative methods and practices of insect and disease control. The following areas of research were to be reviewed:

(a) Use of insect parasites, predators, attractants, and sterile insects.

(b) Use of electrical and physical control devices.

(c) Development of crops resistant to insects and diseases.

(d) Development of safe pesticides and more efficient and less hazardous methods of application.

(e) Better methods of control of diseases and parasites of livestock and poultry.

(4) The degree of coordination between Federal and State agencies in connection with entomology and pest control research and in the approval and use of pesticides, including efforts made to strengthen the well-established and effective Federal-State cooperative relationship in this area.[3]

The completed report was placed on public record in hearings on Department of Agriculture appropriations for 1966, held March 19, 1965.

In conducting the study, the staff interviewed about 185 outstanding scientists and 23 physicians. These experts included biochemists, biologists, chemists, entomologists, nutritionists, pharmacologists, plant pathologists, toxicologists, zoologists, a geneticist, officials of the American Medical Association, members of medical-school faculties, and experts in agriculture, conservation, and public health.[4]

The report's record of the federal, state, and local agencies, the laboratories and universities, the business and conservation groups represented in its interviews leaves little doubt as to the thoroughness and integrity of the staff's work. After the report was made public, those who had been interviewed were asked for permission to have their names made known. Of the more than two hundred persons interviewed, only eight, most of whom are identified with organizations known for their anti-pesticide stand, and two because of official positions, declined to grant permission (two others unfortunately had died in the meantime). The names of those who had no objection to having their names released to the public are listed in the Appendix. Significantly, many of them offered words of high praise for the report. Here are just a few of them.

§

I would like to compliment the staff on the general excellence of this report. It was objective, comprehensive, forthright, and fair and I believe has gone a long way toward setting the record straight on this important and complex subject.

I have read your report and would like to congratulate you on a job well done. Other governmental agencies would do well to operate on such objective principles rather than the crusader's urge which erodes the rights and privileges of the people.

I have read this meticulously detailed and objective report and assure you I will be proud to have my name listed among those interviewed.

I recall the very pleasant but searching interview with your two staff members last August. They indicated a wide knowledge but no bias and at the close of the interview we wondered what direction the report would go. I would wish to commend them both as highly talented interrogators.

What did the investigative staff discover about the experts' opinion of *Silent Spring?* Here is its conclusion.

§

The staff was advised, by scientists and by physicians, that the book is superficially scientific in that it marshals a number of accepted scientific facts. However, it is unscientific in (a) drawing incorrect conclusions from unrelated facts, and (b) making implications that are based on possibilities as yet unproved to be actual facts.[5]

The staff cited several specific examples of misleading statements or incorrect implications. These included:

The allegations that persistent pesticides initiate a "chain of evil."

The charge that chemicals are "little-recognized partners of radiation in changing the very nature of the world."

The implication that because some pesticides have "no counterparts in nature" they must be harmful to man.

The unsubstantiated statement, "To adjust to these chemicals would require . . . not merely the years of man's life but the life of generations."

An exaggeration of the number of new pesticidal chemicals introduced each year and the implication that they somehow require the human body to adapt to them, when in fact "only a few of these chemicals reached man's body, and then only in minute traces, except by accident, suicide, and murder." [6]

The analysis continued:

§

According to Miss Carson, man has now upset a supposedly ideal state of adjustment and balance of life on earth by using chemical pesticides which are staggering in number and "have the power to kill every insect . . . to still the song of birds and the leaping of fish in the streams . . . and to linger on in soil," but of the 394 chemical pesticides registered for agricultural use as of January 1, 1965, the majority, properly applied, do not produce such effects. It was pointed out to the staff by various scientists that the defoliation of many thousands of acres of forests by insects is a conspicuous example of nature out of balance, and that an insect-control program is an effort to restore the balance. Similarly, the housefly with its disease organisms and the Anopheles mosquito with its malarial parasites are just as much a part of the balance of nature as are brook trout, robins, and deer.

The author stated that vast acreages have been treated with chemical pesticides. USDA [United States Department of Agriculture] has reported that less than 5 per cent of the total acreage in the 50 States has had any pesticide treatment, 15 per cent of the acreage planted to crops and 5 per cent of the forests has been so treated, only 0.4 per cent of the acreage available to wildlife has been treated, and less than 10 per cent of the areas producing mosquitoes has been treated with pesticides.

The author stated that chemical pesticides were being used with "little or no advance investigation of their effect on soil, water, wildlife, and man himself," which statement ignored the numerous studies being conducted on such effects. Without proof, the author indicated that pesticides will produce cancer, sterility, and cellular mutations in man, and supposed that pesticides will eventually extinguish plant life, wildlife, aquatic life, domestic animals, and man. Thus, the book created an atmosphere of panic, foretold an impending disaster, and barely mentioned the immensely useful role played by pesticides in the U.S. economy.[7]

The staff summarized its findings on several topics, such as the effects on wildlife, that are taken up in other sections of this book. It is worthwhile quoting here its report on what the American Medical Association and others had to say about Miss Carson's apprehension over the effect of pesticides on man.

§

[T]he staff was informed by the association and by numerous outstanding scientists that, in order to support Miss Carson's thesis that chemical pesticides have harmful chronic effects on humans, she repeatedly drew faulty conclusions from unrelated facts. For example, she correctly pointed out that (a) there has been a gradual rise in deaths from leukemia and (b) there has been an increase in the use of chemical pesticides; she then implied that the pesticides were responsible for the rise in deaths from leukemia. Although there is no evidence that pesticides cause leukemia in humans, there is an excellent correlation between the increase in the number of leukemia patients and the increased use of X-rays and other radiation.

The author also correctly stated that certain pesticides can cause cancer and sterility in animals, and then implied that chemical pesticides cause cancer and sterility in man. However, the American Medical Association and other authorities advised the staff that there is no proof that traces of chemical pesticides cause either cancer or sterility in humans.[8]

The report's conclusion on the effects of *Silent Spring* points out that the book performed a service in alerting the public to the dangers of improper use of pesticides. It also notes that much has been done to pursue the goals the author stressed—the development of more selective pesticides that will kill only one particular pest, the search for physical and biological control methods, and greater study of acute and chronic effects of pesticides in man and animals. "Greater effort has, indeed, been devoted to such problems since the publication of *Silent Spring*," the report notes.[9]

In a review of *Silent Spring*, Cynthia Westcott, plant pathologist widely known as the "plant doctor," answered the point this way:

§

This reviewer, who has worked with entomologists and plant pathologists all her life and who has had a fair amount of contact with manufacturing chemists, cannot concur in this biased viewpoint. . . .

Miss Carson says, "When the public protests, confronted with some obvious evidence of damaging results of pesticide applications, it is fed little tranquilizing pills of half truth. The public must decide whether it wishes to continue on the present road and it can do so only when in full possession of the facts." [10] I say that throughout *Silent Spring* we are given pills of half truth, definitely not tranquilizing, and the facts are carefully selected to tell only one side of the story.[11]

A few paragraphs later, Dr. Westcott noted:
§

I hope that *Silent Spring* will make the average home gardener aware that his package of pesticide has a label with vital information for his safety, but this may be too much to expect. Miss Carson quotes the survey of an industrial firm indicating that fewer than 15 people out of 100 are even aware of the warnings on the containers. My own experience bears this out. I agree with Miss Carson's implication that the juxtaposition of pesticides and groceries in the supermarket makes the average citizen unaware that he is dealing with toxic chemicals. I also agree that we are too apt to use weed-killers as a "bright new toy." All too often I have been called in to diagnose a plant disease that turned out to be 2, 4-D injury. I go along with Miss Carson in abhorring the brown sprayed strips along our roadsides.

However, I am not sure that eliminating the trees and keeping the rest of the natural growth is sufficient for safety. I attended a garden club meeting that had been called to protest roadside spraying. A day or so before the meeting a child was killed bicycling out of a driveway because neither he nor the motorist could see each other through the tangle. There was no further protest, a child was more important than wild flowers.[12]

What is there about Miss Carson's message that evoked such a response that her book remained on the best-seller list for many months and is everywhere quoted with love and reverence? The chord she strikes about nature in her almost unmatchable prose and the resonance this arouses in one's own spirit are doubtless the main reasons. Such a theme, after all, was a great factor in the success of her other works. But some of the most interesting speculation on other aspects of this phenomenon have been furnished by Edwin Diamond, a senior editor of *Newsweek* and the magazine's former science editor, who for a time assisted Miss Carson as she began preparing *Silent Spring*.

Mr. Diamond reminds us that popular distrust of scientists is not a new thing in America. He recalls that years ago a best-seller titled *100,000,000 Guinea Pigs* depicted the perils the nation faced from "an unholy trinity of government bureaucrats, avaricious business-men, and mad scientists" who "had turned American consumers into laboratory test animals. I recall most vividly the danger ascribed to a certain toothpaste, which, if used in sufficient quantity, could cause a hor-rible death." [13]

He also points out that *Silent Spring* followed close on the thalidomide tragedy, when use of a drug resulted in the birth of children with physical defects. He quotes a newspaper interview of Miss Carson in which she said: "It is all of a piece, thalidomide and pesticides. They represent our willingness to rush ahead and use some-thing new without knowing what the results will be." A third point Diamond makes is that any exaggeration tends to attract attention. [14]

Diamond also offers the provocative suggestion

that *Silent Spring* played on a latent public paranoia, the common distrust of others that sometimes takes the form of a belief that all one's neighbors hate one and that sometimes centers on vague fears that "some wicked 'they' were out to get 'us.' " He shares the opinion of many others that Miss Carson's conclusions were exaggerated and were based on the use of half-facts and the omission of full facts.[15]

The opinions of many other people in a position to evaluate the methods and conclusions of *Silent Spring* are included in sections of this work dealing with the issues raised—effects on man, wildlife, and so on. Now, though one dislikes to take issue with a woman of impressive accomplishments and possessed of such a gift for words, it seems appropriate to look at the forces which may have moved her. She evidently had a deep rooted love for nature. For years, she worked for the Fish and Wildlife Service. Her deep feeling is apparent in these words from her earlier book, *The Sea Around Us*.

§

I am deeply interested in the preservation of the few remaining areas of undeveloped sea shore, where plants and animals are preserved in their original relations, in the delicate balance of nature. In such places we may answer some of the eternal "whys" of the riddle of life.

More of her love of nature appears in the following passage from *Under the Sea Wind*.

§

To stand at the edge of the sea, to sense the ebb and flow

of the tides, to feel the breath of a mist over a great salt marsh, to watch the flight of shore birds that have swept up and down the surf lines of the continents for untold thousands of years, to see the running of the old eels and the young shad to the sea, is to have knowledge of things that are as near eternal as any earthly life can be.

Perhaps Miss Carson's mainspring was the age-old desire we all share in varying degrees to recapture the days of one's youth—to be young again with all things as they were, when the sound of birds in springtime brought the keenest pleasure. Miss Carson pictures wonderfully the "good old days" when man was more in tune with other living things, when nature did not need to be controlled to the extent it does today to meet the needs of population growth and world leadership. In this practical world in which we live, however, we must be careful not to let sentiment and nostalgia blind us to the realistic requirements of modern society.

In the first chapter of *Silent Spring*, "Fable For Tomorrow," Miss Carson describes in beautiful and glowing language a delightful make-believe village in a rural setting "where life seemed to live in harmony with its surroundings." The chapter title itself should be sufficient to put an objective reader on notice as to the nature of her story.

Like many Americans, I grew up in such a small rural village. I, too, remember that the grass was green and the birds sang "sweet in the springtime." But my village has changed—mostly for the better. Regardless of sentiment and nostalgia, very few of us would want to return to the inconveniences of those earlier years.

A comparison of my village as it was when I was a small boy with what it is today provides a striking example of the progress we have made through scientific discovery. I remember the "good old days," when to walk barefoot along a dusty country road, to drink cool water from a cistern filled with rain caught from the roof, to read lying flat on one's stomach before an open wood fire by the light of a coal oil (kerosene) lamp seemed to represent the utmost pleasure. Then I had time to listen to the singing of the birds.

I can hear now the toll of the bell in the backyard as members of the family and other workers were called from the field to "dinner" at noon. I remember the bite of the crisp air in the early morning when we had to run out for wood to build the morning fire—wood we had forgotten to bring in the night before. I recall the smoke-house, where cured and hickory-smoked hams and sides of meat were kept for the family's use. I can see now the three-story frame building, then the high school—in earlier years the "Male and Female Normal College"—from which graduated an attorney general of the state, a college president, and many other notables. I can hear the "ding-dong" of the rope-pulled school bell calling for "taking in books." We often hid that rope so that the bell could not be rung.

Yes, I can remember, too, shooting birds with a slingshot and, as I grew older, with a gun. In those days no one worried about stream pollution and we did not hesitate to drink from a still pool in a nearly dry stream.

And now, changes have come to my village. The open fire no longer exists. Heat now comes from gas or oil burners. Though everyone has electric lights, the youngsters seldom read more than is required by the teachers; the temptation to watch and listen to television is too great.

The farm bell is no more. Most of the "hands" have left the farm and now work in factories in town, making radio and television sets, providing electricity and butane gas, manufacturing refrigerators and other conveniences that add to the comfort of life. The few tractor drivers still left on the farm need no bell; for they, like the rest of us, wear wrist watches.

Gone is the smokehouse; it has been replaced by the deep freeze. The school is now a grammar school, built of brick. It is air conditioned, with an automatic electric bell that sounds like a cross between the chatter of a machine gun and the clang of a fire truck. The grammar school graduates go by bus to the East Tallahatchie High School at the county seat.

My village is one in which many people would like to live; but neither I nor they would want to go back to what it was. Above all, I would not want those who have been released from the farm by labor-saving chemicals, machinery, and electricity, who have moved to the city to provide telephones, automobiles, television sets, and other consumer goods, to have to return and dig in the ground to grow food. I would much rather remember those "good old days" while watching television in a modern home, than go back to them with their reduced standard of living.

As I ponder over those "old days" I do remember that we burned on one side while nearly freezing on the other before that open fire. The sweltering heat of summer made it practically impossible to be comfortable. The dusty country road in summer covered us with dust on the shortest trip, and our car got "stuck in the mud" in other seasons.

A flyswatter had a short and hard life, and only a few miles away in the Delta or "bottom," mosquito netting was essential in summer. Really, it must have been my youth which made the "old days" seem so good.

One who reads Miss Carson's writings can easily see how her beautiful prose might lead her readers to convictions far beyond what the facts would justify. Let us look at another part of *Silent Spring:*

§

> One of the most tragic examples of our unthinking bludgeoning of the landscape is to be seen in the sagebrush lands of the West, where a vast campaign is on to destroy the sage and substitute grassland. . . . Even if the program succeeds in its immediate objective, it is clear that the whole closely knit fabric of life has been ripped apart. The antelope and the grouse will disappear along with the sage. The deer will suffer, too, and the land will be poorer for the destruction of the wild things that belong to it. Even the livestock which are the intended beneficiaries will suffer; no amount of lush green grass in summer can help the sheep starving in the winter storms for the lack of the sage and bitter brush of the plains.

These words are beautiful, but completely unrealistic. Sheep are not left on the high plains to starve in the winter storms—the lush green grass of summer is harvested as feed for the winter.

Even so there is magic oftentimes in her evocative words.

§

I know well a stretch of road where nature's own landscaping has provided a border of alder, viburnum, sweet fern and juniper with seasonally changing accents of bright flowers and of fruits hanging in jeweled clusters in the fall. The road had no heavy load of traffic to support; there were few sharp curves or intersections where brush could obstruct the driver's vision. But the sprayers took over, and the miles along that road became something to be traversed quickly, a sight to be endured with one's mind closed to thoughts of the sterile and hideous world we are letting our technicians make. But here and there authority had somehow faltered and by unaccountable oversight there were oases of beauty in the midst of austere and regimented control—oases that made the desecration of the greater part of the road more unbearable. In such places my spirit lifted to the sight of the drifts of white clover or the clouds of purple vetch with here and there the flaming cup of a wood lily.[16]

Doubtless these sprays were for the protection of travelers. I am sure that all who are fat and forty—or over—would like to return to the days of their youth. But deep down we all know that it is youth in a modern society for which we yearn—youth with modern comforts and advantages. Few of us would be willing to sacrifice today's conveniences for unlimited vistas of white clover and purple vetch.

Miss Carson goes further in describing her village of fantasy when she says: "A strange blight came over the area. The people became sick . . . the birds were gone . . . the hens brooded but no chicks hatched . . . the roadsides, once so attractive, were lined with brown."

She then says that such a village does not exist but *might!* She should have known that such situations can and do exist in many places around the world. They

exist largely in backward countries where man has not
learned to make or to use the scientific weapons that
have been developed to cope with disease and pestilence. These nations, almost without exception, have no
chemical pesticides to fight insects and blight.

Miss Carson's melancholy view of a changing world
brings to mind the haunting description of the English
village by Oliver Goldsmith. He, too, deplored the pass-
ing of the "times that were." His wonderful village he
described in "The Deserted Village":

> Sweet Auburn! loveliest village of the plain;
> Where health and plenty cheered the laboring swain,
> Where smiling spring its earliest visit paid,
> And parting summer's lingering blooms delayed.

In Goldsmith's eighteenth-century story, the demon
Trade drew people from the village to the city. His
description of the village after the people left is so
similar to Miss Carson's fears for her make-believe ham-
let that I repeat it here:

> Those matted woods, where birds forget to sing,
> But silent bats in drowsy clusters cling;
> Those poisonous fields with rank luxuriance crowned,
> Where the dark scorpion gathers death around.

Miss Carson has made a contribution to American
literature. But she, along with Henry Thoreau and other
essayists who have advocated a return to nature and
"the simple life," must not lead us into substituting
sentiment and nostalgia for scientific data and facts.

Perhaps Miss Carson's dismay and overstatement both can be traced to a motivation that can best be described as religious. Consider the first paragraph of the second chapter of *Silent Spring*.

> The history of life on earth has been a history of inter-action between living things and their surroundings. To a large extent, the physical form and the habits of the earth's vegeta-tion and its animal life have been molded by the environment. Considering the whole span of earthly time, the opposite effect, in which life actually modifies its surroundings, has been rela-tively slight. Only within the moment of time represented by the present century has one species—man—acquired siginficant power to alter the nature of his world.[17]

In this passage there is obviously deep feeling for the natural order of things. Another good example is her chapter on the balance of nature. Basically the system of interacting life, with the life force of prey and predator and grass and insect keeping one another's numbers in check, is a sacred principle to her. Any-thing that alters the system therefore seems to her to be sacrilegious. Man in this view does not appear to be considered the highest achievement of creation but rather a mere episode, a clumsy interloper whose inven-tions may destroy not only himself but the holy natural order. One may sympathize with this attitude and may be moved by the beauty it creates, but one must be careful of adopting a course advocated in such a spirit without examining it in the light of the value of man himself.

Secretary of Interior, Stewart L. Udall, one of Miss Carson's greatest admirers (she worked for the Bureau of Sport Fisheries and Wildlife of the Fish and Wildlife Service for many years), said in an article, "*Silent Spring* was called a one-sided book. And so it was." [18] He referred to Senator Abraham Ribicoff of Connecticut as the "Silent Spring Senator." Senator Ribicoff opened his committee hearings by saying: "Miss Carson, on behalf of the Committee, we certainly welcome you here. You are the lady who started all this." [19]

I am a member of the Appropriations Subcommittee for National Defense. In connection with this work, I recently visited several of our airfields and missile bases. There I saw the awesome power of man-made fuels, saw demonstrated the terrible destructiveness of our bombs, the unbelievable speed of our fighter planes, loaded with enough destructive force to destroy many cities at one strike. I visited Cape Kennedy where I saw all its equipment demonstrated, with manpower multiplied to the 'nth degree by machines. I was provided a complete briefing and stood at the exact spot where the next space capsule will soon be bolted to the missile.

As I stood there, I thought of Miss Carson's sense of foreboding, quoted by Secretary Udall in his "Legacy of Rachel Carson," in these words: "Now I deeply believe that we in this generation must come to terms with nature." [20]

Truly, I thought, necessary though all of this defense effort appears to be, it is here that Miss Carson's admonition should make its deepest imprint; it is here that nature or natural laws are being turned, not toward a better food supply, a higher standard of living, but toward the destruction of mankind. There I realized her warnings for care and caution in the use of chemicals were timely; however, I also realized that her premonition of doom might well have been directed to this area of destruction rather than to those things which help maintain human life.

I believe all must agree that *Silent Spring*, delightful reading that it is, certainly is not and was never claimed to be a scientific document nor an objective analysis of the chemical–human life relationship. Though we give to it our highest praise for its wonderful prose, for its timely warning, let us move it over from the non-fiction section of the library to the science-fiction section, while we review the facts—in order that we may continue to enjoy the abundant life.

NOTES TO CHAPTER 7

1. Reported in Consumer Reports, XXVIII (1963), p. 37.
2. Quoted in *Conservation News*, XXX, No. 14 (July 1, 1965), p. 8.
3. *Department of Agriculture Appropriations for 1966*, hearings before a subcommittee of the Committee on Appropriations, House of Representatives, 89th Congress, 1st Session (Washington: Government Printing Office, 1965), Part I, pp. 165–166.
4. *Ibid.*, pp. 166–167.
5. *Ibid.*, p. 168.
6. *Ibid.*
7. *Ibid.*, p. 169.
8. *Ibid.*, p. 170.
9. *Ibid.*
10. Rachel Carson, *Silent Spring*, (Boston: Houghton Mifflin Co., 1962), pp. 258–259.
11. Cynthia Westcott, *Half-Truths or Whole Story? A Review of "Silent Spring"* (n.p., n.d.), brochure distributed by Manufacturing Chemists' Association, Inc.
12. *Ibid.*
13. Edwin Diamond, "The Myth of the 'Pesticide Menace,'" *Saturday Evening Post*, CCXXXVI, No. 33 (Sept. 28, 1963), p. 16.
14. *Ibid.*
15. *Ibid.*
16. Carson, *op. cit.*, pp. 64, 65, 66.
17. *Ibid.*, p. 5.
18. "The Legacy of Rachel Carson" by Stewart L. Udall, *Saturday Review*, XLVII, No. 20 (May 16, 1964), p. 23.
19. *Ibid.*, p. 59.
20. *Ibid.*, p. 23.

CHAPTER 8

WHAT IS ZERO?

IN January, 1964, eight dairy farmers in Maryland were suddenly faced with an action that threatened their livelihood. Their milk was withheld from the Baltimore market by their own cooperative, which collects and markets the production of many herds throughout the area known as the milkshed. The reason: The United States Food and Drug Administration had found traces of pesticide in their milk.

Although the FDA itself did not seize the milk, it reported its findings to state and local officials who in turn notified the cooperative. A month later the Baltimore City Health Department suspended the permits to supply milk to the city of two farms in Maryland and one in Virginia. At about the same time the Department of Public Health of the District of Columbia suspended the milk permits of two farms when notified by the FDA that their milk contained illegal residues of a pesticide. In all, the District of Columbia suspended 34 farms in 1964 for this reason. In the previous three years it had suspended only three farms.[1]

The cause was not a sudden, widespread, reckless abandonment of safe use of pesticides. The reason was that the FDA had recently begun using a new, ultrasensitive method of residue detection. The traces now regarded as a threat to the consumer were undetectable only a few months before. What was legal had become illegal not through a change in the law but through an advance in technology. In effect, the agency changed the rules in the middle of the game.

The reader will recall from Chapter 3 that the United States Department of Agriculture and the Food and Drug Administration have responsibility under two different laws, as amended, for different aspects of the procedure for registering a pesticide. If it appears that the chemical will leave no residue on a certain crop, the Department of Agriculture will register it for that crop on a "no-residue" basis. If the pesticide does leave a residue the Food and Drug Administration establishes a finite tolerance, using a generous safety factor, or exempts the product from the tolerance requirement.

If the FDA feels that a pesticide is so toxic that any residue at all might endanger public health it sets the tolerance on certain food products at zero. In practice, as a committee of the National Academy of Sciences has found, the Food and Drug Administration also uses the zero-tolerance provision "when there are not sufficient data to support a greater tolerance"—that is, when it has *not* been proved that certain amounts will *not* harm people. The FDA also applies a zero tolerance "when the use of the pesticide on food crops will not result in a detectable residue within the sensitivity of the best available analytical method after a specified interval between application and harvest for a particular chemical and particular crop." Here is one of the principal sources of trouble.[2]

What is zero? To some the question might seem absurdly simple. It's nothing, that's all. If you can find it, it's not zero. In practice, however, it is not so simple. A scientific testing instrument or procedure has a limit of accuracy for a given material. Sometimes a person might think a test detects a trace of a compound, but if the amount indicated is below the limit of accuracy it might be the result of some slight error in the instrument itself. If the amount of the trace cannot be established in finite terms it amounts to the same thing as zero and the trace can be regarded as negligible.

Before 1962 the Food and Drug Administration could not measure with confidence a residue smaller than a tenth of a part per million (0.1 ppm). When it wished to specify a smaller residue it did not use a smaller figure than that, say .01 ppm, which would be 10 per cent of 0.1 ppm. It specified zero, noting that no greater tolerance was required for the use in question. In effect, this defined the whole range from zero to 0.1 ppm—at this stage still a theoretical matter—as zero, presumably not hazardous to man.[3]

Then came the new detection methods. While in 1955 the limit of sensitivity for detecting DDT in milk was 0.1 ppm, it is now possible to detect 1 per cent of that, .001 ppm, or one part per billion. Nor is it likely that this is the ultimate limit. Even now new advances are making it possible to detect still smaller traces. Identification of a part of chemical residue in a trillion has been reported.[4]

Such amounts are fantastically small. It has been explained that this is like identifying one dime in the federal budget of $100 billion, or one second in 33,000 years of time. The trace of 1 ppm, which is 333,000 times larger than three parts in a trillion, is like comparing a quarter of a mile with the distance to the moon. To deal specifically with the uses in question, a teaspoon of DDT spread over five acres of alfalfa will put 1 ppm of DDT in the hay.[5]

Truly, with our present rapid advances in research results, some day it is likely that man may be able to trace the carbon remaining in the atmosphere from the great Chicago fire or the disturbance remaining from the San Francisco earthquake.

The investigative staff of the Appropriations Committee in its study of the effects of pesticides on public health uncovered a widespread feeling among the experts it interviewed that Food and Drug Administration tolerance regulations were "unreasonable and inconsistent." An example is found in milk. The FDA regards cow's milk as a special food because babies, sick people, and the elderly consume it. Thus it bars any trace of any pesticide from milk in interstate commerce. Representatives of the American Medical Association, however, said there was no medical reason to single out milk for such treatment. They said that invalids and the aged were rarely put on an all-milk diet these days. Bottle-fed babies, they added, are given other foods while very young. Very often these foods are processed baby foods for which the FDA has set finite limits for pesticide residues. A breast-fed baby, moreover, takes in small traces of pesticides with his mother's milk because she eats foods containing legal residues. The studies that have determined this have concluded that the traces caused no ill effects in the babies.[6]

With these facts in hand, let us turn again to the dairy farmers in the Washington and Baltimore milk-sheds. In this area alfalfa is widely raised for feeding dairy cattle. The pesticides heptachlor and dieldrin, both chlorinated hydrocarbons, were recommended by state universities and the United States Department of Agriculture for use in this area to control the alfalfa weevil.

The USDA accepted heptachlor between 1953 and 1959 for use on alfalfa and other crops at rates of application that would not result in more than 0.1 ppm in foods. Heptachlor was barred from alfalfa in 1960 when the Food and Drug Administration cut the tolerance to zero because the residue heptachlor epoxide was discovered and found to enter readily into meat and milk. A zero tolerance for alfalfa was set for dieldrin in 1956.

In the summer of 1960, however, the USDA decided to permit heptachlor on alfalfa on the basis of new data that showed that proper application would leave no residue on cured alfalfa hay. At about the same time the department accepted dieldrin on alfalfa on the basis of similar findings. Both decisions, of course, were based on the residue-detection methods then in use.

On October 11, 1963, the FDA sent a letter to officials across the country advising them that it would begin using the improved testing methods for detecting dieldrin, heptachlor, and heptachlor epoxide. The de-

tection limit it set for milk was .01 ppm, 10 per cent of
the previous level. Curiously, the Department of Agriculture was not notified of this decision until about
three weeks later, when officials heard of the letter from
other sources and requested a copy. After the pesticides
began to be detected in Baltimore-Washington-area
milk, the USDA canceled the registration of heptachlor
for alfalfa in April, 1964, and the dieldrin registration
on the crop three months later.

A representative of an Eastern University told the
investigations staff that the FDA letter caught the university "by complete surprise." It arrived too late, he
said, for the university to adjust its alfalfa-treatment
recommendations for the fall. Many other scientists
mentioned this fault in timing.[7]

When news of the farms' suspension from their
markets appeared in the press, there was widespread
criticism of the fact that one government agency, the
Department of Agriculture, had approved a practice that
led to a ban of the food product as a result of the action
of another agency, the Food and Drug Administration.
The USDA's policy had always been, of course, that no
pesticide should be applied so as to leave an illegal
residue. Though no overt effect was noticed either on
the price of milk or on consumer demand for milk, the
incident can hardly have bolstered the confidence of
the average consumer in the purity of his food supply.

Partly as a result of the lack of coordination
between the two government agencies, the Departments
of Agriculture, Interior, and Health, Education and Wel-

fare have agreed formally to keep one another informed of their activities in the area. Criticisms by the President's Science Advisory Committee have also led to an expanded role for the Federal Committee on Pest Control, on which committee various government bodies are represented.

Congress appropriated $8.8 million in 1964 for indemnity payments for the dairy farmers who had been trapped by the new definition of zero.[8]

Two other incidents illustrate the problems arising from the adoption of new definitions of zero. One involves cauliflower grown on Long Island, New York, in 1963; the other involves cheese produced by a Utah creamery.

The Long Island case began to develop in 1962 when the Food and Drug Administration found very small traces of endrin on cauliflower planted in Suffolk County. Endrin was registered on a no-residue basis because when the manufacturer first requested in 1956 that a tolerance of 0.1 ppm be set for cabbage the FDA decided, on the basis of data supplied by the company, that cabbage at harvest would bear no residue anyway and therefore a tolerance greater than zero was not required. Here again the less sensitive detection methods were in use. When the residues first appeared in 1962, the FDA did not consider them subject to action, but it did report the finding to the Suffolk County Extension Service.

The next year the FDA seized three shipments of cauliflower because of illegal endrin residues. The residues were detected by new methods valid for amounts as small as .03 ppm. It must be said, however, that the FDA had notified the county extension service that it was detecting residues and had asked the service to caution growers about it, but instead the service soon after suggested frequent applications of endrin to control cabbage loopers.

A little later the FDA notified New York State officials of its decision to act against shipments of cauliflower containing over .03 ppm of endrin. The state itself began sampling cauliflower, cabbage, and brussels sprouts before they were harvested and quarantined fields of all three crops because of pesticide contamination.

The Appropriations Committee staff found that the market for cauliflower was reduced by this incident, causing losses not only to the growers directly affected but to others who could not get a normal price for their product. These losses were not compensated by Congress.[9]

The cheese incident developed after farmers in the Delta, Utah, area, contrary to Department of Agriculture instructions, fed dairy cattle with the threshings of dieldrin-sprayed alfalfa raised for seed. The Food and Drug Administration's letter of October 11, 1963, besides setting a detection level of .01 ppm for fluid milk, established a limit of 0.25 ppm for the butterfat of dairy products. (The Utah Department of Agriculture later said the letter was received when hay for the winter had already been harvested.)

An FDA inspection of October 29 showed that the

butter-fat from cheese made by the Brooklawn Creamery Company of Salt Lake City contained 0.5 ppm of
dieldrin, double the new limit. Brooklawn, it discovered,
was buying contaminated milk from 82 producers in the
Delta area. On January 9, 1964, the FDA seized more
than 1000 pounds of cheese that Brooklawn had shipped
across state lines to California. Later, though sampling
of production continued to show residues, the company
refused to keep its cheese off the market and the state
acted to hold back more. The FDA itself seized several
other interstate shipments.

The creamery's manager told the committee investigators that the FDA had never told him that he was
exceeding tolerances and that the seizures had taken
him by surprise. He said he had been unable to learn
from the FDA how the residues were detected but later
learned that the method was a new one. After the first
seizure, he said, he sent samples to private laboratories
that told him they could detect no illegal residues. If he
had known about the new method, he indicated, he
would have taken some action himself.

Staff members learned that the Delta farmers had
been using dieldrin-treated fodder for their cattle for
several years without apparent ill effect. The only
change was the more sensitive detection method. The
incident dealt a severe blow to the farmers and the
economy of the Delta area, as well as to the Brooklawn
Creamery, without compensation.[10]

Though any use of pesticides contrary to the instructions on the label and the recommendations of the

Department of Agriculture is not to be condoned, the following point was made by the staff report:

§

> The original criterion in establishing a tolerance is to provide safety for the consumer of the food against chronic poisons, assuming the individual would eat this food throughout his lifetime, and assuming that the residue occurs on all of the crops at the maximum level at which the tolerance has been granted. However, when a seizure is made by the FDA, the criteria are apparently changed, because FDA seems to act on the assumption that a few servings of the food containing pesticide residues above the legal level would be acutely harmful.[11]

More recently, such actions against milk and other foods containing traces of pesticides have dwindled. It has been reported that the Food and Drug Administration's new testing methods detected minute residues in most milk. This is not surprising in view of the fact that it has long been reported that such traces could be found in virtually all food with no apparent effect on public health. At any rate, there seems to be a necessary easing in the agency's enforcement of the "zero tolerance" provision, not only in milk but in other foods. Perhaps the reason is that the FDA feels it would be difficult to make milk condemnation stand up in court without some sort of tolerance provision.[12]

In 1963, when public alarm over pesticides was fanned to great heat by *Silent Spring*, a report on the use of pesticides was issued by the President's Science Advisory Committee. The report, commonly known as the Wiesner Committee Report after the chairman, Jerome B. Wiesner, recommended several things that seem extreme to many experts, including adopting a goal of eliminating persistent toxic pesticides. Another recommendation, however, urged that the National Academy of Sciences—National Research Council "study the technical issues involved in the concepts of 'zero tolerance' and 'no residue' with the purpose of suggesting legislative changes." [13] Such a study was soon begun by a panel of distinguished experts under the chairmanship of James H. Jensen, president of Oregon State University. The findings of the group, known as the Pesticide Residues Committee, were eagerly awaited by men in government, industry, and agriculture who were convinced that the current practices were absurd. The Pesticide Residues Committee released its conclusions in June, 1965, about three months after the Appropriations Committee's report was issued.

The panel's findings were unequivocal. It declared: "The concepts of 'no residue' and 'zero tolerance' as employed in the registration and regulation of pesticides are scientifically and administratively untenable and should be abandoned." [14]

The committee explained:

§

The rapid advances in analytical chemistry have now made it possible to detect minute amounts of residue where previously none had been found. The development of these highly sensitive instrumental methods is necessary in the broad field of analytical chemistry, but it is illogical to associate a tolerance value with the ability of chemists to detect smaller and smaller amounts. The Committee considers that the registration of pesticides for uses on foodstuffs should relate more to considerations of safe use than to the limitations of analytical methodology. The small residues that may now be detected in many food products are more likely to be due to uncontrolled factors, such as drift, spills, soil contamination, and residues from previous crop treatments rather than to any recommended use. The possible presence of such inadvertent residues must be considered in registration, setting of tolerances, regulatory enforcement, and recommendations for use. Proposals for registration on the basis of "negligible residue" and "permissible residue" are set forth in this report.[15]

Under these proposals, a maximum acceptable daily intake level would be established for each pesticide. If a residue on a certain food was less than some small fraction of this level it would be regarded as toxicologically insignificant and therefore negligible. Studies already exist on levels of consumption of different foods that could be used in setting prudent intake limits. Pesticides for which some tolerance is allowed under current practice would still be related to the overall daily intake level, but a particular food could have traces above the "negligible" level. The committee proposed that the term "tolerance" be abandoned in pesticide administration "because it is often erroneously interpreted to indicate the maximum level of intake which can be safely tolerated in a physiological sense" while it actually means "a legal limit, based on the minimum requirement resulting from technological use, and is actually only a small fraction of the estimated no-effect level in man." [16]

In view of the experiences described in this chapter with the new detection methods, some of the pesticide committee's remarks about these methods are enlightening:

§

Presumptive recognition of pesticide residues in check, control, or untreated samples may also arise for a variety of reasons relating to the analytical procedure, such as the presence of compounds causing interference in the specific reaction used in determination, or from spurious electronic signals if instrumentation is involved. . . . The presence of minute background amounts of pesticide in untreated produce makes it difficult to obtain a true check or control sample, and hence reduces the precision with which small residues can be measured. . . .

Recent advances in the techniques and instrumentation of chemistry have resulted in the development of analytical methods that can detect some residues and their reaction products at levels in the parts per billion range. These newer methods are far more sensitive than the best procedures available only a few years ago and, thus, have complicated the administration of no-residue and zero-tolerance registration.

In view of these new developments and the extreme shortage of experienced personnel, it is not surprising that there are many new problems associated with the present state of the art. Disturbing variations exist in the reproductibility, reliability, and sensitivity of analyses performed by different operating residue laboratories. The profusion of analytical methods and equipment, as well as the variety of procedures for sampling, concentration, and isolation are matters of real concern. Further, the lack of a uniform terminology has added to the confusion in the interpretation and comparability of results.

It is important that the distribution of dietary intakes of pesticides be monitored on a national scale. This will require full use of modern survey and sampling techniques, of continued standard inter-laboratory comparisons, and of competent statistical analysis of results. The statistical and analytical difficulties associated with current efforts along these lines substantially reduce the reliability of the findings.[17]

After such observations it is hardly surprising that many of the committee's recommendations concerned analytical methods. These included a call for the government to specify the method to be used for analyzing residues when it registers a pesticide and not to change the method without notice.[18]

If any further word is needed on this point, we have the testimony of George P. Larrick, commissioner of the Food and Drug Administration itself. Mr. Larrick, appearing before a Congressional committee, said that when the original law with its zero requirement for pesticides was passed the methods of analysis were far less refined than they are today.

§

> Later, when Congress considered the same questions with respect to food additives and with respect to color additives, the Department [of Health, Education and Welfare] and we [the Food and Drug Administration] recommended that the type of zero tolerance which is included in the pesticide law is unrealistic and unworkable. . . . I do think the zero tolerance in this pesticide law, as it stands, does not make good sense. . . . In all instances where it can be done, I think the whole question should go through the tolerance-making procedure and a finite tolerance should be set . . . on milk, too.[19]

The weight of all this evidence leaves no doubt that the "zero-tolerance" and "no-residue" policies should be revised without delay. The "negligible-residue" and "permissible-residue" provisions recommended by the Pesticide Residues Committee of the National Academy of Sciences—National Research Council are sensible. Here is a policy that is scientifically sound and administratively practical. Congress must act speedily to enact these recommendations before the existing unrealistic provisions are again used to threaten the livelihood of an innocent farmer.

NOTES TO CHAPTER 8

1. *Department of Agriculture Appropriations for 1966,* hearings before a subcommittee of the Committee on Appropriations, House of Representatives, 89th Congress, 1st Session (Washington: Government Printing Office, 1965), Part I, p. 179.
2. Pesticide Residues Committee, *Report on "No Residue" and "Zero Tolerance"* (Washington: National Academy of Sciences—National Research Council, 1965), p. 3.
3. *Agriculture Appropriations,* I, 173.
4. Taken from speech by Dr. Andrew Breidenback, "Detection, Identification and Measurement of Pesticides," made at the National Academy of Sciences—National Research Council "Public Symposium on the Scientific Aspects of Pest Control," November 18, 1964, Cincinnati, Ohio, in which Dr. Breidenbach quotes from a statement by Mr. Bernard Lorant, Vice President, Velsicol Chemical Company, made at the Federal Water Pollution Control Enforcement Conference on Pollution in the Lower Mississippi River and its Tributaries, sponsored by the U.S. Department of Health, Education and Welfare, May 5 and 6, 1964.
5. *Ibid.*
6. *Agriculture Appropriations for 1966,* Part I, p. 174.
7. *Ibid.,* pp. 179–181.
8. *Ibid.,* pp. 180, 181, 192.
9. *Ibid.,* pp. 181–183.
10. *Ibid.,* pp. 183–185.
11. *Ibid.,* p. 173.
12. "The Facts on Pesticides—Setting the Record Straight," extension of remarks, in *Congressional Record,* CXI, No. 199 (Oct. 27, 1965), p. A6128.
13. The President's Science Advisory Committee, *Use of Pesticides* (Washington: Government Printing Office, 1963), p. 20.

14. Pesticide Residues Committee, *op. cit.*, p. 16.
15. *Ibid.*, p. 6.
16. *Ibid.*, pp. 9–11.
17. *Ibid.*, pp. 5–6.
18. *Ibid.*, p. 16.
19. *Interagency Coordination in Environmental Hazards (Pesticides)*, hearings before the Subcommittee on Reorganization and International Organizations of the Committee on Government Operations, U.S. Senate, 88th Congress, 2d Session (Washington: Government Printing Office, 1964), Part IX, pp. 1905–1906.

CHAPTER 9

THE GREAT FISH KILL
AND OTHER ALARMS

$\smile$

O N March 19, 1964, the *Los Angeles Times* anounced that pesticides, apparently seeping from farms, had caused the deaths of millions of fish in the Mississippi River. "Mystery Deaths of Millions of Fish Traced to Midwest Farm Pesticides," the headline proclaimed. "Federal and Louisiana scientists now have discovered that the massive and continuing fish death toll is caused by pesticides, particularly dieldrin and endrin, which have been spread on farm crops in the Midwest and South," the story read. On March 22 a headline in the *New York Times* said flatly, "Poisons Kill Fish in the Mississippi; Millions Die of Pesticides Draining from Farms." The dispatch said: "A scourge of toxic synthetic chemicals is killing untold millions of fish in the Mississippi River Basin. Pesticides draining from the farmlands of Missouri, Arkansas, Tennessee, Mississippi and Louisiana have resulted in widespread fish deaths over the last four years, Federal experts say." Papers across the country carried similar stories. Conservation publications took up the case as the "biggest pesticide disaster to date." [1]

The story was not true. Millions of fish had died

159

and pesticides were implicated; but as the case later developed it was the alleged discharge from a plant that manufactured the pesticide endrin, not runoff from agricultural land, that was accused, and it was by no means certain that the vast majority of the fish involved had died from pesticide poisoning anyway. As is always the case with reckless charges, however, the charge attracted much more attention than the effort to correct it. Doubtless the incident damaged the case for agricultural pesticides more than anything else since the publication of *Silent Spring*.

The great fish-kill controversy began in the fall of 1963 when great numbers of dead and dying fish were discovered in the lower Mississippi River Basin, including the Atchafalaya River. A large kill had occurred in the same waters in 1960, and in the two years following kills of smaller size were reported. According to the report of the Surveys and Investigations Staff of the Committee on Appropriations, House of Representatives, which is the only objective summary I know of the confusing events that followed, the State of Louisiana on November 18 asked the Public Health Service to determine the cause of the kill. About two weeks later two scientists from the agency went to Louisiana to begin their investigation.

The kill was huge. Estimates by the State of Louisiana place the total at five million for one species alone, the menhaden, an inedible saltwater type used in making fertilizer, meal for animal feed, and oil for industrial uses. All these were in the Mississippi River, which supports saltwater fish in this area. Some 75,000 freshwater fish were also estimated to have died in the Mississippi and 100,000 more in the Atchafalaya, where only freshwater fish live. The freshwater varieties were identified as catfish, buffalo, and carp, all edible species. Menhaden, however, accounted for more than 96 per cent of the total kill.

In the course of an investigation lasting several months the Public Health Service scientists satisfied themselves that pesticides were the cause. They found significant quantities of endrin, dieldrin, and DDT in fish tissues. The level of endrin was established in the blood of six or eight freshwater fish and it was decided, on the basis of laboratory feeding tests, that this level was high enough to have killed them.

The scientists examined only one menhaden, however, which apparently had decayed to the point that an analysis was difficult. Nevertheless, the final Public Health Service finding was that endrin killed the menhaden.

On March 10, 1964, an information officer of the Public Health Service received word from the service's Robert A. Taft Sanitary Engineering Center in Cincinnati that endrin had been identified as the cause of the fish kill. He drafted a news release that began: "The U.S. Public Health Service has informed the State of Louisiana that water pollution involving toxic synthetic organic materials appears to be the cause of massive and continuing fish kills in the lower Mississippi." The draft also said that several toxic compounds had been found, including the pesticides endrin and dieldrin, which are used to protect Midwestern and Southern crops, and that the levels of endrin alone in the blood of the fish studied were high enough to have killed them.

The PHS sent copies of the proposed release to the Department of Agriculture, the Federal Pest Control Review Board, and the State of Louisiana on March 17 and asked for their recommendations for changes. On the basis of these recommendations the release was changed to read: "Several chemical compounds have been found in significant quantities in dead and dying fish and in the water environment, including at least two substances so far unidentified and two pesticides, endrin and dieldrin." Two major passages were deleted: "used to protect Midwestern and Southern crops" and "The levels of endrin in the blood of the fish studied would alone have been sufficient to cause death." The release was issued March 19.

The PHS information officer said, however, that on March 17, the same day that the draft was sent out for suggestions, he received calls about it from two newsmen, including one from the Washington correspondent of the *Los Angeles Times*, and from a representative of a chemical company. The *Los Angeles Times* man asked for and was denied an exclusive story, then said he would file a story anyway, on the basis of the draft. The result was cited at the beginning of the chapter. The *New York Times* account appeared three days after the revised release was issued, but the correspondent may have obtained some of his material from other sources than the release and the earlier draft.

On April 1, Surgeon General Luther Terry, head of the Public Health Service, said in a speech in Cincinnati:

§

You are acquainted, of course, with the mysterious and frighten-
ening puzzle posed by the death of millions of fish in the Mississippi River Basin over the last four years. Now our scientists
working here at the Taft Sanitary Engineering Center and elsewhere have identified the culprit responsible—infinitesimal traces
of chemical pesticides draining from farmlands throughout the
watershed.

The Secretary of Agriculture, Orville Freeman, took
exception to the statement in a letter to Anthony J. Celebrezze, Secretary of Health, Education and Welfare, and
received in reply a letter conveying the regrets of Mr.
Celebrezze and Dr. Terry for any implication that the
materials found in the Mississippi River came wholly
from runoff from farmlands or from any single source.[2]

Also in April the Department of Agriculture held
a series of confusing hearings in Washington, Memphis,
and Baton Rouge, but heard no evidence from the 84
witnesses that the endrin involved came from farm use.
By this time the PHS was beginning to point a finger at
a Velsicol Chemical Corporation plant near Memphis
that made endrin. The Department of Health, Education and Welfare also called a four-state conference in
New Orleans May 5, 1964, which decided that endrin
was responsible but that there was no evidence that it
came from agricultural runoff.

A graphic description of the controversy at this
point is furnished by the magazine *International Science
and Technology:*

§

The political pressure became so intense that the Agriculture Department felt compelled to call hearings on whether

the use of endrin, aldrin and dieldrin should be restricted or banned. The hearings did little to clarify the situation, for, in fact, the department was at a loss as to how to proceed. In confusion, it handed the problem over to a hearing examiner, who served more as a toastmaster for introducing and dismissing witnesses than as a judge seeking to establish facts. The result was a series of statements by government and private witnesses, with no attempt to resolve the mounting contradictory evidence and claims.

The Department of Health, Education, and Welfare, meanwhile, had jumped into the procedural confusion by calling a conference under the Federal Water Pollution Control Act—the first step in formal pollution abatement action. The hearing in New Orleans in early May was somewhat of an advance over the Agriculture Department inquiry, in that it permitted at least a confrontation in which the opposing sides briefly and inconclusively debated their conflicting evidence and claims. From the start, however, the hearing was dominated by the Public Health Service, which presented most of the testimony and controlled the procedures. In the end, the conferees went along with the conclusions that had been submitted in advance by the Public Health Service, finding that endrin was responsible for the fish kills and that the industrial wastes from the Memphis area were at least one source of the pesticide. The Public Health Service may well be correct in its findings, but the conference adopted the conclusions in a rather hectic finale. Indeed, things had moved so fast that industry representatives walked out of the hearing room without seeming to realize that a portentous indictment had been entered against their products.

On a matter of such great potential significance—not only to the chemical industry, but also to the farmers and, indirectly, to consumers—there was need for a more orderly procedure to establish the facts beyond any doubt before federal action was taken.[3]

The account of the hearings in *International Science and Technology* pointed up an unappetizing aspect of the affair—differences among government agencies. This not only included conflicts among elements of the Departments of Agriculture, Interior, and Health, Education and Welfare. It also included, according to the article, friction between the Division of Water Supply and Pollution Control, which aspired to become a semi-autonomous agency within HEW, and other officials of the Public Health Service, a branch of HEW and a group which did not support this aim. The article went on to state:

§

In a situation of such potential significance as to demand calm, dispassionate consideration, government agencies were vying with one another to extend or protect their jurisdictions, leaking reports to a Senate committee to buttress their cases, reaching conclusions before the scientific evidence was publicly available, withholding information from one another and tossing out accusations at an industrial firm which they later had to retract. As one Agriculture Department official aptly summed up the situation: "It is like a group of sovereign powers attempting to negotiate a treaty for the good of the nation."

Even if the suspicions of political motivations are groundless, therefore, one of the principal conclusions to come out of the Mississippi fish-kill situation is more political than scientific. In brief, the conclusion is that the government—from the White House Office of Science and Technology down to the hitherto obscure Division of Water Supply and Pollution Control—is not organized to get at the facts and reach the policy decisions in such a highly complex, technical area as the public. health hazard presented by the agricultural use of pesticides.[4]

The establishment of the Federal Water Pollution Control Administration in October, 1965, and its subsequent transfer to the Department of the Interior in May, 1966, is intended to help, but this may create more problems than it solves, though the several departments are cooperating in broad studies of the effects of pesticides on the environment. Nevertheless, there is no assurance that, if such a situation ever arises again, the resources of the federal government can be deployed in

an efficient, unbiased, reliable manner to get the facts
and take appropriate action.

When some of the endrin implicated in the Mississippi River fish kill was first reported to have come from
a plant in Memphis, the question was immediately raised
as to why fish had died only below Baton Rouge,
hundreds of miles downriver, which daily releases 17
million gallons of sewage into the stream. The company
denied that leakage from its plant was responsible and
challenged the analysis of the PHS scientists. This is
how a spokesman described the theory:

§

> This is like firing bullets from Memphis 500 miles down
> the Mississippi, miraculously aimed so they would hit nothing
> until they reached Louisiana. It also would be akin to firing a
> cannon in Chicago from Randolph Street down the sidewalks of
> State Street at high noon, taking care to hit only a rat peeping
> around the corner at 127th Street.

Witnesses attempting to answer this point in the
USDA hearings said, in effect, that the chemical was
convoyed between two mysterious substances, x and y,
for hundreds of miles and then was suddenly released.
This sounded like something out of Grimm's fairy tales,
and references to x and y were soon dropped.[5]

Velsicol and the Shell Chemical Company, which
has a plant in Colorado that is the nation's only other
producer of endrin, began intensive research to find out
for themselves if endrin killed the fish, and if not what
did. The committee staff's report cited three experts

familiar with the fish-kill incident who believed the
PHS result was based on insufficient research; George C.
Decker, a University of Illinois entomologist; S. Leary
Jones, executive secretary of the Tennessee Stream Pollution Control Board; and L. Dale Newsom, an entomologist at Louisiana State University. Other scientists,
the report said, held similar opinions.[6]

In all the discussion, it should be pointed out,
there was no indication that the pesticide, if it did kill
the fish, presented a hazard to human health.

The uncertainty over the cause seems not to have
affected Secretary of the Interior Stewart L. Udall, however. In an article published in the summer of 1965, he
placed the area of the kill from Memphis southward, a
discovery that seems not to have been mentioned in
the controversy earlier, when the kill was located south
of Baton Rouge. He told his readers flatly that the fish
had been accumulating endrin and other hydrocarbons
in their fat over a long period. With cold weather
approaching, he said, the fish stopped feeding and re-
absorbed their fat, releasing highly concentrated chemicals into the bloodstream. "Paralysis, followed by death,
came quickly," he concluded.[7]

Massive fish kills, of course, were known long before
the invention of endrin and happen somewhere every
year. Captain John Smith's party saw dead fish all
around their boat and lining the shores of the river during a trip up the Potomac in June, 1608. In 1882 millions of huge dead and dying unicorned tilefish littered

the surface of the sea between Cape Cod and Chesa-
peake Bay. A careful study concluded that great schools
of them had died when a freakish mass of cold water
enveloped them, changing the temperature faster than
they could tolerate. In this incident the species was
almost wiped out.

Fish are killed when snow covers the ice over a
lake or stream during the winter, because this cuts off
the light that plant organisms need, even then, to produce the oxygen the fish must have. Shad are killed by
the school when they enter shallow streams from which
the oxygen has been driven by the heat of the sun. Fish
are killed at sea by the upwelling of deep water carrying volcanic gases. Fish are killed by the "red tide," the
abnormal concentration of a tiny plant organism that
gives off a poison. They are regularly killed in the Chesa-
peake Bay when low-oxygen deep water is swept into
shallow areas by storms.

There remain the man-made causes of fish kills.
Underwater explosions are one of these. But the most
significant, particularly in inland waters, is pollution.[8]
The members of a traveling symposium on the pesticide
problem sponsored by the National Academy of Sciences
in November, 1964, saw a vivid demonstration of the
pollution menace—samples of the filth from myriad
sources, derived from 250,000 gallons of the water from
several different American rivers. To remove the cover
of a container and smell the revolting odor was enough
to make anyone realize that we must act to protect our
water supply without delay. Yet though contaminants
may at times, at places, cause fish kills, and pesticides

may even be among the contaminants, the same symposium was told by an authority that there is no known way
to make absolutely sure of what killed a given dead fish.
A meticulous survey of the fish-kill phenomenon made
the same point:

§

> Pollution in the form of industrial toxins, bilge oil, pesti-
> cides, and sewage certainly cause fish kills, some of which are
> of great magnitude. Unhappily, scientists have often found that
> it is difficult to discriminate between those causes having a
> natural origin and those resulting from man's heedlessness, as
> careful examination of dead fish rarely reveals the cause of
> death.[9]

At the beginning of its study the Public Health
Service considered and ruled out depletion of oxygen,
sudden changes in water temperature, diseases caused
by bacteria and viruses, and metallic poisons as causes
of the Mississippi fish kill. Some persons interviewed on
the issue by the Appropriations Committee staff, however, believed the cause was simply industrial waste.[10]

Meanwhile, in October, 1964, another massive fish
kill occurred in the Atchafalaya Basin. It was many times
larger than the kill there the year before (when most
of the dead fish were in the Mississippi)—but it attracted very little attention. The reason was that the
cause was obviously Hurricane "Hilda." The storm swept
decayed vegetable matter into the canals and bayous and
its decay used up the oxygen in the water, suffocating
the fish. The kill was halted in November when oxygen-
bearing Mississippi water was fed into the basin through
the locks at Port Allen.[11]

Perhaps the best-known incident involving public fears over the effect of a pesticide occurred before the publication of *Silent Spring*. This was the case involving cranberries and the weed-killer aminotriazole. The incident, fed by sensational publicity from the Food and Drug Administration, caused damage to the cranberry industry that lasted at least four years.

The Department of Agriculture had accepted aminotriazole on a "no-residue" basis in January, 1958. For cranberry bogs the specified time of application was seven to ten days after harvest, allowing almost a year before the next crop ripened for residues to dissipate. In May, 1959, the Food and Drug Administration denied a petition for a tolerance because tests showed that the chemical caused cancer in animals.

The FDA soon learned, however, that cranberry growers in Washington and Oregon were using aminotriazole to control weeds during the growing season, in violation of the USDA instructions. As the crop matured the agency collected and tested samples from all over the western cranberry region and prepared to act.

In October, officials of Ocean Spray Cranberries, Incorporated, the national cooperative of cranberry producers, visited the Food and Drug Administration to assure the agency that it was acting to prevent contaminated berries from reaching the market. The Ocean Spray representatives pointed out that the cooperative on its own initiative had kept 3 million pounds of berries from reaching consumers in 1957, when growers had used the herbicide before it had even been registered.

The Department of Health, Education and Welfare,

however, believed that the cooperative's program was not fully effective because it found traces of aminotriazole in two of the region's first seven shipments. On November 8 the department decided to make all the facts public and to make an all-out effort to screen the cranberry crop of Oregon and Washington. Ocean Spray officials agreed to cooperate. But on November 9, when they evidently saw an advance copy of the news release, they urged that the statement be delayed 48 hours to see if a catastrophe affecting the entire industry could be avoided. The request was refused and the announcement was made in the form of a news release at a press conference conducted by Arthur S. Fleming, Secretary of Health, Education and Welfare.

The release that had rightly alarmed the cooperative urged that no sales be made of the cranberry crop from Washington and Oregon because of their possible contamination by aminotriazole, which causes cancer in the thyroid of rats when introduced into their diet. It also called for suspension of sales until the cranberry industry had submitted a workable plan to segregate the contaminated berries. The release described the contamination already detected and said that it would take until about Christmas to bury the contaminated berries "with the use of bulldozers." The statement said that although there might be a minute proportion of a carcinogen, or cancer-causing substance, that would be safe in foods consumed by humans, FDA scientists did not know if this was a fact nor how to establish a safe tolerance.

Thereafter the FDA seized about 300,000 pounds

of cranberries, or about 0.25 per cent of the 1959 crop.

Despite later attempts to restore normal marketing procedures and consumer confidence, sales and prices plummeted sharply in the Thanksgiving-Christmas season, when the industry does most of its business. In January, 1960, it was reported that there were a million 100-pound barrels of surplus cranberries, valued at about $21.5 million. It was also reported that there were other losses that could not be estimated, resulting from such things as the reluctance of bankers to extend credit to growers and the economic effect of the nonutilization of cranberry land. At President Eisenhower's request, Congress approved the payment of $10 million to growers who had sustained losses on uncontaminated berries.

Ocean Spray's figures show that while the average price received by a grower for a barrel was $11.95 in 1958, the price dropped to $8.68 in 1959, including the indemnity. The average price was $8.87 in 1960, $8.14 in 1961, and $9.41 in 1962. Not until 1963, when the average was $11, did the figure approach its former level.[12]

Thus, by using a scare technique similar to that of *Silent Spring*, an agency of government caused serious damage to an important segment of agriculture, innocent members as well as guilty. One can hope that if ever again a situation of this sort arises, some way can be worked out to deal with it that will fully protect the public health but will not bring harm to those without blame.

Things apparently have reached the point where,

whenever somebody sees a dead fish or bird, he immediately leaps to the conclusion that the cause was a pesticide.

An example is the fish kill in the Missouri River between Kansas City and St. Louis in May, 1964. An article in the St. Louis *Post-Dispatch* of May 28, reported: "Tuesday a conservation agent counted 660 dead fish floating past the bridge at Miami, which is about midway between Kansas City and Jefferson City. Carcasses have been seen as far west as the Kaw River at Kansas City, but it is not known whether the kill extended into Kansas." Were pesticides the cause? Although this article and similar ones in other newspapers in Missouri and across the nation did not explicitly say so, they made enough references to pesticides to suggest that they might very well have been the culprit.

Three days later the *Post-Dispatch* reported that investigators had found that the oxygen content of the water at points along the river was far below normal. "At Miami, Missouri, midway between Jefferson City and Kansas City, where great numbers of dead fish were seen floating down the river Tuesday, the oxygen content of water was 1.6 parts per million as compared with a normal of 5.5 parts per million. Oxygen ranged downward from 5.5 points all the way from St. Louis to north of Kansas City." The reason apparently was that heavy rainstorms in the Missouri Valley had brought unusually large amounts of organic matter into the stream, and the decay of this matter took unusual amounts of free oxygen from the water.

Analysis of water samples and dead fish by the

Public Health Service uncovered small traces of dieldrin and DDD, a close relative of DDT, but the concentrations were below the levels believed to be harmful to fish. No traces of these or any other chemicals were found in the fish themselves.[13] The PHS told the State of Missouri that it was unable to determine the cause of the fish kill. H. C. Clare of the PHS said the probable cause was the lack of free oxygen in the water.

In an example concerning birds, Allen Quayle of the Landscaping Maintenance Office of the California State Division of Highways in San Francisco explained bird deaths on the highways in an article that appeared in the February 18, 1964, issue of the *Oakland Tribune:*

§

The annual spring binge of the birds is on. Robins and cedar wax wings are lushing it on the masses of red berries on pyracantha and toyon bushes. Many of these "threats" are along freeways planted for landscaping. This is true in Contra Costa County among other places.

So when motorists who are friends of the feathered fiends notice them dead by the roadway they call up the Division of Highways. They accuse the Highway Department of deliberately spraying the bushes with a food fowl poison. . . .

The birds are gluttons. They not only stuff themselves with the berries until they are too full to fly, but the mature berries are intoxicating.

In July, 1964, Walter Trohan cited a similar situation in his widely read syndicated column:

§

Last fall numbers of dead thrushes were found on the grounds of the National Health Institutes which seemed to disclose that Miss Carson's book was not fiction but prophecy. This week it was found that the thrushes had not been done in by pesticides, as had been suspected, but that the birds dined unwisely and too well on fermented crabapples! While they flew off in high spirits, the thrushes killed themselves by flying into walls, wires, and other objects.

Until the facts were known, these bird deaths had been used as ammunition in the antipesticide campaign.

The people of America must understand that pesticides today are essential to modern farming. To deprive the farmer of these vital tools would be to cripple American agriculture and if agriculture is crippled, so are the markets of industry and labor. In a social order that is now able to function with only 8 per cent of its population left on the farms, the consequences would be ruinous. If there are unknown hazards to health arising from the agricultural use of pesticides, they must, of course, be identified and corrected. No one in industry, government, or anywhere wants to be responsible for undermining the health of the population or threatening the future of man and other life on earth. On the other hand, food production must not be curtailed because of the remote possibility of danger when careful studies show that there is no overt hazard at all. The reckless charge is a powerful and irresponsible weapon in a campaign apparently intended to wrest the precious pesticide tool from the hands of the farmer. One moral from the publicized incidents involving pesticides seems to be: Don't jump to hasty conclusions and make charges based on guesses rather than facts.

This is not to say that pollution of air and water does not exist; for, of course, it does. Pollution is part and parcel of man's unplanned and unthinking change of his environment; and particularly is it a part of the subject under discussion in *Silent Spring* and here. Public opinion here seems to be on the move toward action. This public temper can be good if held in balance. It can do more harm than good if not kept on an even keel.

Pollution comes from many sources and becomes greater as our population increases; unless we take corrective action, it will become worse as we become more and more industrial. We do have pollution of the air and water and apparently are going to do something about it. These facts lead me to point to some of the factors with which we must deal as we attempt to meet this problem.

§

The fact that air is essential to life is as old as knowledge. The fact that polluted air can cause discomfort is probably just as old. As soon as primitive man moved his fire into his cave, he certainly became aware of air pollution in the form of smoke. He also probably soon learned to reduce the smoke in his cave by careful placement and stoking. He then decided to accept some smoke in return for the warmth and convenience of the fire nearby.

We have been weighing pollution against convenience ever since. Now we are beginning to realize that more than convenience is involved and that the air around us is not a limitless sea into which we can continue to pour waste without serious consequences.

Our health and our well-being are threatened.

Thus did the *Agriculture Yearbook of 1963: A Place*

To Live, describe one of the serious problems of our day, air pollution.

The increasing pollution of our water unquestionably is a threat to fish and health. This became a matter of public concern in the United States in the late nineteenth century, when virulent typhoid epidemics appeared in various cities. The then new science of bacteriology identified many of these outbreaks as the result of contaminated water supplies. The public outcry against pollution was great. Public health officers attempted to meet this challenge in two principal ways.

The first was to select certain streams for waste disposal and to reserve other, and protected, streams for municipal supplies. This is the method followed by communities fortunate enough to own or control adequate watersheds. However, with our increasing population, it is virtually impossible today for one city to live separately and apart from another. While one city may protect its water supply, it will be adversely affected if those in adjoining areas do not do likewise.

The other method was the filtration and disinfection of water. This has permitted many cities to have reasonably safe and palatable water, even from such heavily polluted sources as the Missouri, the Mississippi, and the Ohio rivers.

While these systems have worked for many years, we now face a period when we must give full attention to water pollution, or else pay substantial penalties in the future. We have some 30,000 sewerage systems and industrial complexes pouring waste into our streams. Included are 10,000 municipal sewerage systems, serving more than 100 million people, which dump sewage into the waterways. Twenty-five per cent of this load is without any treatment whatsoever.

Pollution degrades the physical, chemical, biological, and esthetic qualities of the water. The degree depends upon the kind and amount of pollution in relation to the extent and nature of reuse. Pollution can be just as effective as a drought, or excessive withdrawals, in reducing or eliminating water resources.

Over 2600 new or enlarged sewage treatment works are needed to serve 27.8 million persons living in communities presently discharging untreated or inadequately treated sewage. Another 2598 new sewage collection systems and treatment works are required to serve a population of 5 million living in urban areas where individual disposal systems have failed to function properly.[14]

By the year 2000, thirty-four years from now, we will be around 330 million Americans as against today's 194 million. We will have nearly doubled the quantity of sewage going into our streams and protecting the public health will really be a problem.

Today's 194 million Americans are abusing our resources so far as our use and handling of water is concerned. Our lakes and rivers have become catch basins for the residues of our factories, automobiles, household and agricultural chemicals, for human wastes from thousands of villages, towns, and cities. How well we clean up this situation and learn to handle it without restricting man's means of providing our high standard of living may well determine the future of our nation.

As we approach this problem we must keep in mind that the power to control water quality or quantity is not only the power to make or break business but is a power over the life of the nation itself.

Since water is an absolute essential to health and to all man's activities, any group we set up to control water on any basis, by restrictions for protection of its quality or quantity and use, must have not only the cooperation and co-ordination of all departments and agencies; but all interests must be represented. The Department of Agriculture and the Department of Health, Education and Welfare, whose interests are tied together, should have a place in any such group, as should the Department of Commerce; but these are not enough. The states and municipalities must be represented so that the varied interests of all our citizens may be recognized and provided for, including riparian rights, established use, and the determination of priority to use. All this need carries with it the problem of built-in bureaucracy, of too many cooks, yet there is seldom an easy answer to a difficult problem.

If we closed all our manufacturing plants, that would greatly improve the purity of the water in our streams; if we stopped driving automobiles, just think what that would do to improve the atmosphere—and a single departmental head could have done that under several bills; if we could return to the 800,000 population level of this country at the time it was discovered by Columbus, nature would be able to largely eliminate the pollution problem. But with 194 million people we could never live in the simplified way of that day. Neither can we ask nor could we force the residents of New York City to quit eating, quit living, and quit breathing while we clean up the Hudson. The same is true for Washington and the Potomac, as well as the people of thousands of towns and villages. The power to set standards is the power to control, yet some Members of Congress have urged that such power be granted to a single government department.

Agriculture's claims and responsibilities for the use of water are second to none, for agriculture provides our food, clothing, and shelter, the basic necessities for life. In addition, agriculture has a great responsibility in the use of water, for land is the great gathering place and reservoir for storage of water. Just a few years from now we will need three times the water we use today, all of which points up the need to protect and manage the quality and quantity of our water supply.

In our work with the Appropriations Subcommittee for Agriculture, we find the close cooperation and coordination of efforts by both the Corps of Engineers and the Soil Conservation Service are necessary in watershed and flood control programs, both of which are highly essential to water protection. We would not expect a skilled surgeon to use only one instrument for all operations, nor a mechanic to fix our car with a sledge hammer. Thus it is with water pollution; we must use the tools required for the job; and most importantly, we must keep the factory running in the process and not turn the surgeon's scalpel over to the mechanic or vice versa.

To do the cleaning up job on pollution, we must call on industry, on the federal, state, and city governments, and on individuals. We need financing and regulations; in the meantime, we must maintain a sense of balance, so that we do not tear up more than we correct. We are not merely limited to the practical but to the possible.

NOTES TO CHAPTER 9

1. *Department of Agriculture Appropriations for 1966,* hearings before a subcommittee of the Committee on Appropriations, House of Representatives, 89th Congress, 1st Session (Washington: Government Printing Office, 1965), Part I, 187.
2. *Ibid.,* pp. 185–187.
3. *International Science and Technology,* No. 31 (July, 1964), p. 79.
4. *Ibid.,* p. 78.
5. Transcript of Hearings before the Secretary of Agriculture in the matter of Registration of the Economic Poisons Aldrin, Dieldrin and Endrin under the Federal Insecticide, Fugicide and Rodenticide Act, Memphis, Tennessee, April 16, 1964.
6. *Agriculture Appropriations for 1966,* Part I, p. 186.
7. "Our Seesaw Battle Against a 'Silent Spring,' " *True: the Man's Magazine,* vol. 46, no. 339 (August, 1965), pp. 71–72.
8. Romeo Mansueti, "The Murderous Team," *Skipper,* vol. XXIV, no. 6 (June, 1964), pp. 24, 41–42.
9. *Ibid.*
10. *Agriculture Appropriations for 1966,* Part I, p. 185.
11. Louis A. McLean, "It Happened in America—Almost," speech before Western Agricultural Chemicals Assn. in Portland, Ore., January 13, 1965.
12. *Agriculture Appropriations for 1966,* Part I, 175–179.
13. *Ibid.,* pp. 187–188.
14. *National Municipal Policy* (Washington: The National League of Cities, 1966), pp. 121–122.

CHAPTER 10

CAN NONCHEMICAL
METHODS DO THE JOB?

C ALIFORNIANS faced disaster in the 1880's.
The citrus groves, a mainstay of the state's economy,
were threatened with destruction by a tiny, almost im-
mobile sucking insect called the cottony-cushion scale.
It had first appeared in the state in 1872, apparently introduced from Australia, and in 15 years had covered the
entire citrus belt, ruining crops and killing trees. The
threat appeared so desperate that many growers pulled
up their trees and planted other crops.

Then an entomologist sent to Australia by the
United States Department of Agriculture discovered an
insect that gorged on the scale—and nothing else.
Shipped to California in 1888, the vedalia beetle found
the surroundings to its liking and quickly made itself at
home. In two years the scale was under control and has
never since become a threat. For an investment of $5000
in a scientist's trip, citrus growers and consumers have
received dividends in the millions.[1]

This case, the first successful international experiment of its kind, is the classic example of one type of
nonchemical pest control. It has stood for decades as a
reminder that nature itself may provide weapons to

183

combat the problems it presents. Research on such approaches continued even when the development of potent chemical weapons required much work on the most effective ways to apply them. Now, though much remains to be done in this area, the older nonchemical methods are again attracting increased attention. Perhaps this is partly because of rising public apprehension over the widespread use of pesticides. But perhaps it is also because the chemical road has become well worn and proven and other areas, boasting several remarkable achievements, now offer more promise of excitement and discovery. The Department of Agriculture estimated in 1963 that only about a third of its research on insect control concerned the conventional chemical approach. Another third involved various nonpesticidal approaches, and the remainder dealt with basic biological research and other subjects. The department noted that a major shift in emphasis had taken place over the previous five years.[2]

The achievements of nonchemical and special chemical methods of pest control are most welcome. Surely everyone rejoices when a crop strain is developed that is resistant to a serious fungus disease; the disease will never again be a problem, and the farmer will never again have to buy a fungicide—at least for that one disease—and invest his time and equipment in applying it. No scientist, farmer, or politician is wedded to pesticides. They are expensive and difficult to use. Research on alternative control methods should be continued and accelerated. Possibly the time will come when chemical pesticides can be largely eliminated. If so, those engaged in agriculture will be the first to use the new methods.

But the farmer's situation must be understood as it exists now, not as it may exist in the future. He already benefits from a variety of biological methods of pest control; some, such as resistant strains, are so effective that the troubles they prevent are almost forgotten. There are many other problems, however, for which no non-chemical control exists. If one is discovered the farmer will adopt it gratefully. Until then, if he knows an investment in a pesticidal chemical will repay him in a bigger, higher-quality crop, he will use the chemical. When it appears that omitting the pesticide will result in some possibility of a crop failure he will also use it, just as a prudent man carries insurance. And if he faces, say, five insect pests, any one of which may ruin his crop, he will not refrain from spraying because one of the pests is already checked by a natural enemy that will also be destroyed. This last point seems to be overlooked in some discussions.

What are the various nonpesticidal methods of controlling pests? What have they accomplished, what promises do they hold, what research is under way on them, and what are their drawbacks?

One of the methods of controlling insects that has attracted wide attention is the release of masses of sexually sterile members of the pest species. The sterile insects compete with normal ones for mates, resulting in infertile matings. The overall population of the insect declines, and each succeeding generation is infiltrated with sterile members until at length only infertile eggs are laid and the species dies out.

This method was used with spectacular success in the late 1950's to eradicate the screwworm from the southeastern United States. The screwworm is a fly maggot that infests wounds and sores of cattle, feeding on the flesh. A bite by another fly or a tick is enough to give the pest a start. A heavy infestation can kill a full-grown steer in ten days. The pest caused losses in the Southeast estimated at $20 million a year.

But the screwworm is sensitive to cold weather and can survive only in near-tropical climates, like that of southern Florida. Department of Agriculture scientists, who had worked out the sterility-control theory, devised methods of raising large numbers of screwworms and sterilizing them with gamma radiation. They seized the opportunity presented them when the severity of the winter of 1957–1958 confined the pest to a small section of Florida. In 17 months 3.5 billion sterile screwworm flies were released and the pest was wiped out. In Texas and New Mexico, where the problem is different because the insect can re-invade more easily from the south, the method is nevertheless being used with great success.[3]

That the device has not since been widely used is evidence that control through sterility is difficult. Some insects mate many times, not just once, like the screwworm fly. Not many kinds of insect pests exist in relatively small numbers in a relatively restricted area. Of those that do, ways must be found to raise the insect in huge numbers for the screwworm-method to be applied. For many insects, sterilizing them with radiation reduces their vitality as well as their reproductive powers and they are unable to compete for mates with the unsterilized.

The approach continues to be explored in many different areas, however. Another pest that has been dealt with successfully this way is the melon fly, a problem in Hawaii. In 1962 and 1963, the Department of Agriculture tested the method on the little Pacific island of Rota, about 40 miles northeast of Guam. The natural melon-fly population was reduced about 75 per cent with bait sprays. Then from 4 million to 10 million sterile flies were released each week. Within three months the fly had disappeared from the island.[4]

Research is centering on other species of tropical fruit flies. Tests have shown that the reproductive potential of the Mediterranean fruit fly, the Mexican fruit fly, and *Drosophila* fruit flies can also be greatly diminished by the sustained release of sterile insects.

Another method of sterilization uses chemosterilants—chemicals that sterilize. Used with baits or attractants, they can do their work without raising the problems of mass production and release of sterilized insects. But a major problem here is the safety of chemosterilants. Their toxic properties have to be investigated fully, and some have produced a leukemia-like reaction in cattle. When they come into more general use, steps will be taken to protect human health by making sure that only the insects or pests to be sterilized will be able to approach them. One problem is that use of at least one widely tested chemosterilant, apholate, has been found to produce a resistant strain, just as insecticidal chemicals do.[5]

Much interest is also being shown in such non-pesticidal chemicals as sex attractants, baits, and the like. The approach is not new; as early as 1929, traps containing lures were used to catch Japanese beetles, which were destroyed. The powerful sex attractant of the female gypsy moth has now been synthesized and, under the name gyplure, is now readily available and inexpensive. It has undergone a large-scale test as a bait in traps scattered by airplane. In 1962 a sex lure for the pink bollworm was found which, when perfected, may be used in scattered traps to improve detection of that scourge of cotton. Early detection is essential to effective control of the bollworm since an infestation does not become evident until the damaged cotton bolls fail to open.[6]

Virgin females of other pests—the tobacco horn-worm, cockroaches, for example—have also been found to use sex attractants, and attempts to synthesize them are under way. Such attractants, besides serving as baits for traps or poisons, conceivably could be scattered broadcast to confuse a pest's mating activity. They may also prove valuable for luring insects to traps where they will be sterilized by radiation or chemicals. Other types of lures, such as methyl eugenol, trimedlure and cue-lure, attract males of the oriental, Mediterranean, and melon fly.[7]

A dramatic example of combining a lure and a pesticide was the eradication program for the Mediterranean fruit fly in Florida in 1956. In an earlier infestation, in 1929, it spread over a wide area and threatened to wipe out the entire industry. A program that engaged 6000 persons, largely for the destruction of infested trees and fruit, achieved eradication. When the fly reappeared in 1956 it was eradicated by a force of only 800 men using malathion and trimedlure. The experience gained in that campaign helped wipe out small-scale returns in 1962 and 1963.[8]

Substances have also been found in plants and animals that attract insect pests to them. The boll weevil, for instance, is drawn to the cotton plant by a specific substance. This discovery may lead to a new way to control this pest.[9]

Everyone has seen moths and beetles swarming around a street light in summer. Many insects find light fatally attractive, including many destructive pests— codling moth, European corn borer, the moths of the tobacco and tomato hornworms, and the cigarette beetle, for instance.

Research is in progress on the use of light traps to control the tobacco hornworm. A more common use, however, is early detection of pest outbreaks and invasions. The responses of different insects and different sexes of insects to continuous and flickering ultraviolet, argon-glow, and incandescent lamps are under study.[10]

Repellents are not being neglected. A search is under way for something that might be included with insecticides to make bees shun sprayed fields. More effective ones, with no sacrifice in safety, are being sought for military use. Similar research in the past has already led to effective chemicals that are widely used in civilian products.[11]

Several other ways of fighting insects use completely nonchemical methods. One of the chief of these is the use of a natural parasite, like the case of the vedalia beetle described earlier. Another good example of the international use of this method involves the citrus blackfly, a serious fruit pest discovered in Florida in 1934. Quickly eradicated in Florida, it became established in Mexico and spread as far as Texas.

In 1943 Mexican and United States experts found the principal parasite of the citrus blackfly in Cuba. But although the parasite was effective there it was not adapted to the hot, dry climate of Mexico. In 1949 an American entomologist went to India to search for more natural enemies of the pest. Through his efforts and those of Mexican scientists four species of small wasps, admirably suited to the Mexican climate, were distributed over a large part of Mexico's citrus-producing area. These natural enemies now keep the fly under excellent control in much of Mexico, minimize the need for pesticides, and reduce the hazard of the fly's spreading into the United States.[12]

It must be emphasized, however, that the parasite

method is a limited one. Many pests that are native to America, not imported, flourish here in spite of such enemies, and the search for possible insect controls is slow and laborious. The approach suffers many failures, as shown by the fact that of more than 650 species collected and brought into the United States in the last seventy-five years, about 100 have become established and about 20 are helping to control serious insect pests.[13]

There are also dangers that must be watched in the introduction of predators and parasites for pests. The hoped-for friend may turn out to be as much of a threat as the original enemy.

There are several classic examples of disastrous results from introducing predators. One is the mongoose in Hawaii. Hawaii became infested with rats after they arrived as unlisted passengers on the earliest ships to stop there. The favorable climate, a lack of natural enemies, and the abundance of food made life easy for the rodents. In 1883 someone had what was thought to be a bright idea: Perhaps the mongoose, native to India, could be persuaded to rid Hawaii of its problem. Brought to the islands of Hawaii and Oahu to protect the sugar plantations, the aggressive little killer attacked not only rats but poultry, game birds, and other forms of life. By 1892 the mongoose had become so destructive that legislation was enacted to prohibit its being kept in any part of the Hawaiian Islands. It almost destroyed several native bird species, including the Hawaiian duck, the duck-rumped petrel, and the shearwater. Now the Hawaiian Division of Fish and Game is trying to exterminate the mongoose.[14]

Another example of unexpected problems from introducing an alien life form to an area is the nutria, an aquatic South American rodent that was imported to Louisiana to be grown for its fur. Several escaped, and now millions of them are found in the swamps of Louisiana and neighboring states. The nutria now seems to be almost beyond control or eradication.

Diseases of insects have also been used to control pests, and a strong search for others is continuing. It has been known for more than a century that insects are susceptible to diseases, just as other forms of life are. One of the first animal diseases in which a microorganism was identified as the cause was a fungus disease of silkworms.[15]

The milky disease was discovered on the ground-dwelling grubs of Japanese beetles in New Jersey in 1933. A way was developed to cultivate the disease organisms on live grubs, which then were ground, dried, and mixed with talc. Milky disease is commercially available and can be established in a Japanese-beetle area simply by applying this dust to grassy areas. In one application where the insect was thick but the disease was absent, colonization of milky disease reduced the grub population from 88 per square foot to negligible proportions in a few years.[16]

A bacterium called *Bacillus thuringiensis* is commercially available for control of the alfalfa caterpillar and a number of other agricultural pests, and a type of virus is used to control the European pine sawfly. Development of diseases as insect controls, however, is a slow process. They are usually expensive. In many cases a disease does not take effect on a farm pest until the crop is practically destroyed. Unexpected variations in weather can cause a failure in this method, as can a slight error in timing.[17]

Some scientists interviewed by the investigative staff of the House Committee on Appropriations had doubts about whether it was advisable to spread disease agents as insect controls with little or no monitoring. They said that the anthrax bacillus, which infects man, is related to some of the insecticidal bacteria, and that bacterial frequently undergo mutation when produced in artificial media or when subjected to adverse environments. Viruses are believed to cause some forms of cancer and should not be distributed without sufficient knowledge of them, it was argued.

Other scientists, however, pointed out that a true insect-disease organism has never been known to infect man, that no harmful mutation of an insect-disease organism has ever been detected, and that microorganisms, mostly beneficial or absolutely harmless, abound in man's environment. The Department of Agriculture exercises the same rigorous control over such biological materials as it does over the introduction and use of insecticidal chemicals.[18]

Insect control can also be accomplished by a completely different method—development of insect-resistant crop varieties. Perhaps the best-known example was the introduction in 1942 of a variety of wheat resistant to the Hessian fly, which had often destroyed the entire crops of Midwestern wheat growers. An alfalfa variety has also been developed that is resistant to the spotted alfalfa aphid, and corn strains have been produced that are resistant to the corn earworm and the European corn borer.

Resistance to an insect may result from several factors. The plant may have tougher stems and leaves, or it may not have the food value the insect needs, or it may have hairy leaves and stems that make it difficult for the insect to feed. Corn that grows long, tight husks presents more difficulties for the corn earworm than types that have short, loose husks.[19]

With this method, of course, the difficulty is that it takes a long time to find and develop a resistant trait in a crop, and then it takes still more time to breed the trait into the different varieties that may be required for successful planting in different sections of the country. Even though government scientists alertly keep stocks of crop plants on hand from all over the world with characteristics that may prove useful in time, there still may be some delay between the appearance of a new pest and the development of a resistant strain.[20]

Slight variations in farming practices can also make a difference between a scarcity and an abundance of some pests. Moderately late plantings of corn suffer less damage than early plantings from the corn rootworm in the South and from the European corn borer in the North. Plowing under the cornstalks in the fall also cuts down the European corn borer, which spends the winter as a caterpillar in the stalk. Spring cultivation of vineyards in the Lake Erie region buries the grape berry moth and prevents it from leaving the ground. Plowing similarly buries some eggs and pupae, uncovers others that need protection, and buries crop remnants that could harbor still other pests. Crop rotation helps starve out insects that can survive on only one kind of plant. Very seldom, however, can such practices, valuable as they are, provide the degree of control necessary for productive agriculture.[21]

Developing disease-resistant plants, one of several promising approaches to insect control, is the principal area of research in the problems of plant diseases. The Department of Agriculture puts five times as much effort into developing resistant varieties as it does into chemical control of plant diseases.

The number of disease-resistant varieties being grown testifies to the method's success. Ninety per cent of the watermelons grown in the Southeast are resistant varieties developed by the Department of Agriculture. A variety of Eastern lima bean resistant to downy mildew has eliminated the need for chemical controls. Forty per cent of the soybean acreage is planted to varieties that are resistant to one or more diseases. More than 90 per cent of the durum wheat grown is of a variety highly resistant to black stem rust.[22]

Cultural and environmental practices also help control some plant diseases. Until a few years ago peanut growers covered the base of the plant with dirt to control weeds, but research traced the cause of a serious stem rot to this practice. Carefully controlled cultivation

to keep loose soil away from the plant and use of herbicides to control weeds is now recommended. As in insect
control, farming practices such as crop rotation, sanitation, tillage, and fertilization can be manipulated to
reduce crop infection.[23]

Nonchemical methods also have an important role
in the control of diseases of forest trees. The most common tree disease is heart rot, which enters through an
injury of some sort and affects older trees more readily
than young ones. Care in forestry practices to avoid
wounding sound trees, fire prevention, and harvest of
trees at the proper age can, it is estimated, reduce heart
rot 75 per cent.[24]

Despite the spectacular success of chemical herbicides mechanical controls are the only method used on
some 80 per cent of United States crop land. Such
methods have held the attention of the Department of
Agriculture since it began farm research more than a
century ago, and they remain a fruitful area.

Usual methods of control are mowing the tops of
weeds to keep them from producing seeds and cultivat-
ing crops to starve weed roots. Many states require control of noxious weeds in fallow fields and other unculti-
vated areas. Regulations exist to assure a farmer that
he will not plant weeds along with his crop seed.[25]

In something of a switch, the government imported
two beetles that chew a certain plant to pieces—but in
this case the plant was an undesirable weed, and so the
insects, instead of being regarded as dangerous pests,
are viewed as benefactors. The plant is the Klamath

weed, which somehow found its way to the range lands of the West around 1900. It is also known as goat weed and, in its native Europe, as Saint-John's-wort. Klamath weed displaces desirable range plants, and when cattle eat it they become scabby, sore-mouthed, unthrifty, and irritable. At its height the Klamath weed infested about 2.3 million acres in California and some 2 million acres in neighboring states. Chemical control was difficult because the weed was so widespread and thrived in inaccessible places.

Following the lead of foreign research on the same problem, California experts in 1944 imported specimens of two leaf-eating beetles that Australian scientists had found in Europe and successfully established at home. After a year of tests to make sure that some other American plant would not be more to their liking, colonies of the insects began to be released. In a few years the weed's spread had been checked and its economic impact, at least in California, had been eliminated.[26]

Since then promising insects that attack puncturevine, Scotch broom, and other plant pests have been imported with some success. But, interesting and effective as the method is, the limitations are obvious. Not many of our weeds originated abroad and migrated here without their parasites. There is a long, long road ahead before a significant number of the weeds that now plague a farmer can be controlled by insects.

According to the report of the Agricultural Research Service, U. S. Department of Agriculture, under the direction of Dr. George W. Irving, promising developments have been made with an insect virus which promises control of the cotton bollworm, the tobacco budworm, and the corn earworm.

Another new development is a synthetic hormone which retards development of the larvae of the yellow mealworm.

Mass rearing of many insects for research purposes has been accomplished, increasing the output of insects twelve times. This should help greatly, since a great number are needed to control insects by sterile insect release, application of pathogens reared on insects, and for the release of parasites and predators.

Large numbers of insects are needed for advance research to develop new insecticides, pathogens, repellents, and resistant plant varieties, to identify sex attractant for synthesis, and to obtain basic knowledge of insect physiology and behavior.

An aphid repellent, aluminum foil, has been found which provides an effective control of mosaic disease.

Tests have been made which have disclosed the response of the boll weevil to different colored lights, which is one step toward nonchemical control.

The department has been able to control the sting nematodes which destroy transplanted tomatoes by careful rotation of tomatoes and marigolds and crotalaria.

Blight disease of cotton and the black rot disease of tobacco are being met by development of disease-resistant varieties.

Volume production of virus has now been proven practical. This "know how" would have saved us millions of dollars in the outbreak of foot-and-mouth disease in Mexico a number of years ago.

Coccidia are now grown in a test tube. This will reduce cost of research, assuring pure cultures, thereby greatly enhancing control studies.

Toxicity studies are being made experimentally which will save large sums annually. This breakthrough will help with lambs where up to 25 per cent may have deformities from eating skunk cabbage. Up to 100 per cent deformities may occur in calves eating the lupine plant.

Research is a continuing process. Results are slow but sure. New problems arise as fast as old ones are answered.[27]

One cannot cover the subject of pesticides and their alternatives without considering the report of the Environmental Pollution Panel of the President's Science Advisory Committee, issued late in 1965 under the title *Restoring the Quality of Our Environment*. Pesticides are a central concern of the report, and one of its major sections deals with ways to control pests without pesticides. The air of authority with which it presents its findings and recommendations makes it seem probable that it will have as great an impact as *Silent Spring* and perhaps more, at least among government officials.

The panel of scientists proceeded under the assumption that any pollution is bad, regardless of whether it is harmful or not. "There should be no 'right' to pollute," it declared.[28]

Since a subpanel's report dealt exclusively with the problem of increasing quantities of carbon dioxide in the atmosphere, one might ask whether it shouldn't also

be stated that there is a right to breathe. Perhaps such
an objection makes light of the very serious long-range
questions the panel posed very effectively, but it does
indicate that even here the question is one of degree.
For pesticides, too, it would seem reasonable to
acknowledge that there are levels at which the presence
of DDT, for instance, will do no harm and therefore can
be regarded as negligible. It also seems doubtful that
questions of this order should be dealt with under the
topic of "pollution," which is a word that carries a built-
in judgment against the materials to which it is applied.

The references to pesticides in different sections of
the report, prepared by subpanels, display a surprisingly
wide range of difference in attitude, in the very tone
with which pesticides were discussed.

In the general panel's report the tone regarding
pesticides is severe. In places, perhaps, it is as guilty
as *Silent Spring* of making a general judgment on the
basis of an isolated, nonrecurring incident. The evidence
for the judgment is not presented. This section also
seems to display, however, an awareness that the case is
not one-sided and that there is a sphere where the presence of pesticides is not hazardous. It says, for instance,
on the subject of pesticides and human health (emphasis
supplied):

§

Chlorinated hydrocarbon and phosphate ester pesticides
have been detected in many surface and ground waters, in
amounts ranging up to a few parts per billion. *These small concentrations are not known to be a threat to human health.* On rare
occasions, higher concentrations of pesticides appear in potable
waters, usually as a result of industrial discharges. *Human
illness traced to pesticides in public water supplies has not been*

reported, but examples of illness from domestic well contamination may have occurred.[29]

I am not aware that there has ever been a case of a poisoned well from the normal use of pesticides. Aside from this objection, the effort to avoid suggestions of harm where none can be shown is evident, a welcome contrast to the techniques of *Silent Spring.*

Two of the report's 13 recommended "principles" deal with pesticides and are widely accepted, though the report indicates urgent need for future acceptance. One calls for integrated use of pesticides and other control methods; the other urges that unnecessary use of pesticides be avoided. Five of the 28 recommended "actions" and three of the 19 proposed areas of intensified research also concern pesticides; these recommendations are rather variable in value.[30]

Of the 11 subpanel reports, two particularly concern us—the one on soil pollution and the one on environmental pollution.

"Preliminary data from the U. S. Department of Agriculture monitoring program, now in its second year, indicate that pesticide residues are not present at high concentrations in soils with high pesticide-use history," reports the subpanel on soil contamination. The subpanel notes the detection of dieldrin and heptachlor residues in milk in the East after the development of highly sensitive new detection methods and neglects to mention the problem of zero tolerance that this episode illustrates. But it adds that this has not caused a soil-pollution problem. The soil pollution it does note concerns limited areas of especially heavy use, such as orchards, and, generally, use of the older arsenical pesticides. Other forms of soil pollution, including salinity, radioactive fallout, and industrial wastes, are also discussed, serving to keep the pesticide question in perspective.[31]

The subpanel on health effects of environmental pollution was primarily concerned with airborne pollution, including not only smog but atmospheric lead and asbestos. It did not mention pesticides.

Where, then, did the panel get the material that led to its general recommendations? From the reports of two other subpanels, one on "Effects of Pollutants on Living Organisms Other Than Man," and one on "Improved Pest Control Practices." Of the 218 pages of the whole report that are devoted to the work of the subpanels, 100 pages are devoted to these two reports.

The report on other living things bears heavily on pesticides. Most of what it says is dealt with in other sections of this book. It places a mistaken emphasis, though, on the fact that agricultural use of insecticides reduces the number of insect species around plants. One might think that their major concern should have been saving the plants.

In its discussion of wildlife, assumptions about accumulation of pesticides and sublethal individual effects are not adequately substantiated. The report does not recognize the obvious increases in game populations in areas where pesticides are heavily used. "The extent to which wild bird and mammal populations have been affected by pesticides is largely unknown except for the numerous obvious examples of mortality," it says.

"The more basic and critical population changes that operate through a series of complex interrelationships over a period of time are difficult to recognize, more difficult to predict." This is like saying you can't tell whether Houston is bigger than it was a decade ago by the census figures, you have to analyze it block by block.[32]

The report on "Improved Pest Control Practices," on the other hand, appears to be a thorough, imaginative, and valuable contribution to the field of nonchemical pest control, which the report calls "bioenvironmental control." If one overlooks a certain lofty tone, one can find an excellent summary of the present state of the art and a wealth of valuable suggestions for the course of future research.

It is notable that the report emphasizes the need for continued use of pesticides as long as they are the only way to cope with a problem:

§

For certain pests there are no immediate prospects for development of effective bioenvironmental methods. Certain conventional pesticides are indispensable for maintaining current food and fiber production and the health of man and animals. Furthermore, it should not be assumed that all pesticides have adverse effects, are persistent, and have a high toxicity to man or warm-blooded animals in general.[33]

Again, in another connection, we are reminded:

§

It should be borne clearly in mind, however, that biological control is now being used against all pests for which natural enemies are known, and the present level of pesticide use is necessary in many instances. Before pest control costs can be

reduced and the drawbacks of pesticide use, including environmental pollution, avoided, further research support for biological
and other bioenvironmental control will be required.[34]

The reference in this passage to "environmental
pollution" brings us to a major objection to this report,
however. As we have seen, the other sections of the
overall report do not document an assertion that pesticides contribute significantly to pollution of the
environment.

In general, the report of the Environmental Pollution Panel is valuable in many ways and contains bril-
liant work. But it is seriously flawed by a failure to
reckon with the *degree* to which the mere presence of
a "pollutant" causes harm. It is also seriously flawed by
a lack of balance, of proportion; some problems are
treated at great length, others are barely mentioned and
then dropped. Bearing as it does the prestige of the
President's Science Advisory Committee, the effect may
be by implication to harm pesticides more than they
deserve, judging merely by what the report says in
words.

One of the more recent reports on this entire subject was presented to the Appropriations Subcommittee
for Agriculture by Dr. George L. Mehren, Assistant
Secretary of Agriculture, who supervises expenditure of
the more than $30 million being spent annually on
research on the insect, pest and pesticide problem. Dr.
Mehren reported that the Department had made real
progress in its effort to develop means of control other
than pesticides and in educating the public on the

proper use of pesticides by television, radio, news releases, and pamphlets.

The Assistant Secretary said cooperation between the Departments of Agriculture and Health, Education and Welfare was now excellent.

His testimony, contained in Part I, Hearings before the Appropriations Subcommittee for Agriculture in February, 1966, covers the broad subject of pesticides, their use, and misuse rather thoroughly, together with alternative methods of control, including research now being carried on.

Dr. Mehren's report fills a book—and a worthwhile book at that. His conclusion was to reaffirm the Department's findings that:

§

. . . from necessity pesticides will continue to be the major pest control weapons in the foreseeable future. However, their use has created special problems such as: some seventy species of insects in the United States have developed resistance to chemicals used against them. The *misuse* of some chemicals may result in harm to beneficial insects, birds and other wildlife as well as fish. . . .

Non-chemical pest control methods, including biological, cultural and mechanical, are both very old and very new. These methods sometimes are sufficient, but more often their most effective use is in combination with chemical control. . . .

NOTES TO CHAPTER 10

1. C. P. Clausen, "Parasites and Predators," in U.S. Department of Agriculture, *Insects: The Yearbook of Agriculture, 1952* (Washington: Government Printing Office), p. 380.

2. *Interagency Coordination in Environmental Hazards (Pesticides)*, hearings before the Subcommittee on Reorganization and International Organizations of the Committee on Government Operations, U.S. Senate, 88th Congress, 2d Session (Washington: Government Printing Office, 1964), Part I, Appendix II, p. 180.

3. Rachel Carson, *Silent Spring* (Boston: Houghton Mifflin Co., 1962), pp. 279–282; Environmental Pollution Panel, President's Science Advisory Committee, *Restoring the Quality of Our Environment* (Washington: The White House, 1965), pp. 278–280; "Facts about Screwworm Eradication," Agricultural Research Service, USDA (Washington: Government Printing Office, January, 1963).

4. "Eradicating the Melon Fly," *Agricultural Research*, Vol. 12, No. 2 (Aug., 1963), p. 5.

5. *Department of Agriculture Appropriations for 1966*, hearings before a Subcommittee of the Committee on Appropriations, House of Representatives, 89th Congress, 1st Session (Washington: Government Printing Office, 1965), Part I, pp. 199–200; "Can Insects Develop Resistance to Chemosterilants?", *Agricultural Research*, Vol. 13, No. 3 (Sept., 1964), p. 13.

6. "Effects, Uses, Control, and Research Use of Agricultural Pesticides," in *Agriculture Appropriations for 1966*, Part I, pp. 198–199; "USDA Scientists Identify Pink Bollworm Sex Attractant" and "Detection of Pink Bollworm Moths Possible with Natural Attractants," U.S. Department of Agriculture Press Releases, April 19, 1965 and December 12, 1962.

7. *Interagency Coordination*, Part I, Appendix II, p. 181.

8. *Ibid.*, Part I, Appendix I, pp. 142–145.

9. "Can Boll Weevils Be Led Astray?", *Agricultural Research,* Vol. 11, No. 3 (Sept., 1962), p. 7.
10. Howard Baker and T. E. Hienton, "Traps Have Some Value," in U.S. Department of Agriculture, *Insects,* p. 408; *Agriculture Appropriations for 1966,* Part I, p. 199.
11. *Interagency Coordination,* Part I, Appendix I, p. 10.
12. "Beating the Blackfly," *Agricultural Research,* Vol. 3, No. 6 (Dec., 1954) p. 12.
13. *Agriculture Appropriations for 1966,* Part I, p. 197.
14. Paul H. Baldwin, Charles W. Schwartz, and Elizabeth Reeder Schwartz, "An Economic Status and Life History of the Mongoose in Hawaii," *Journal of Mammology,* Vol. 33, No. 3 (Aug., 1952), pp. 335–356.
15. Edward A. Steinhaus, "Infectious Diseases of Insects," in U.S. Department of Agriculture, *Insects,* pp. 388–390.
16. Ira M. Hawley, "Milky Disease of Beetles," in U.S. Department of Agriculture, *Insects,* pp. 394–397.
17. *Interagency Coordination,* Part I, Appendix I, p. 21.
18. *Agriculture Appropriations for 1966,* Part I, pp. 199–200.
19. C. M. Packard and John H. Martin, "Resistant Crops, the Ideal Way," in U.S. Department of Agriculture, *Insects,* p. 430.
20. *Ibid.,* pp. 433–434; *Interagency Coordination,* Part I, Appendix I, pp. 22–23, 26–27.
21. W. A. Baker and O. R. Mathews, "Good Farming Helps Control Insects," in U.S. Department of Agriculture, *Insects,* pp. 437–440; *Interagency Coordination,* Part I, Appendix I, p. 23.
22. *Ibid.,* p. 26.
23. *Ibid.,* p. 27.
24. *Ibid.,* p. 28.
25. *Ibid.,* p. 25.
26. James K. Holloway and C. B. Huffaker, "Insects to Control a Weed," in U.S. Department of Agriculture, *Insects,* pp. 135–137; Environmental Pollution Panel, *op. cit.,* p. 261.
27. From statement by Dr. Herman A. Rodenhiser, Deputy Administrator, Farm Research, Agricultural Research Service, during hearings on 1967 Budget for U.S. Department of Agriculture, February 14, 1966.
28. Environmental Pollution Panel, *op. cit.,* p. 16.
29. *Ibid.,* p. 4.
30. *Ibid.,* pp. 16–38.
31. *Ibid.,* pp. 74–90.
32. *Ibid.,* pp. 209–211.
33. *Ibid.,* p. 230.
34. *Ibid.,* p. 269.

CHAPTER 11

THAT WE MAY LIVE

In conclusion, we must realize that the highest standard of living in the world is possible in this country because it takes so few people to produce food for the rest, thus leaving a great proportion of the population free to provide for us the other products we use and consume. This situation sums up the secret of the great economic development of the United States in the past several decades. But it also poses a most serious threat to our national welfare. With so few people on the farm, the voice of agriculture is weak in the legislative halls of a majority of the states and of the nation. No longer do the producers of food and fiber figure prominently in the planning of our elected officials. This leaves a major task for those of us who are convinced that the national welfare depends on a sound and healthy agriculture.

Unless our urban population understands agricultural problems, future generations could go hungry; our nation could go down to ruin as did the city-states of the past. After all, the eventual loser will be the consumers whom those in agriculture serve.

The press in urban areas has not been covering agricultural news and problems. In my own personal

208

experience, my farm speeches and the professional agricultural meetings I address receive very little coverage, despite the interviews. My remarks on space missions or bases, as a member of the Appropriations Subcommittee for Defense, however, receive a very different treatment.

The real tragedy is that editors know their urban readers prefer to read about local bases and guided missiles. My own experiences certainly point up the problem we now have in getting the American consumers who do not live on the farms to understand. The consumers must be convinced that the good health of agriculture is vital to their own good health and welfare.

What this also means is that we must get over to the 92-plus per cent, the consumer group, that this is more than a mere agricultural problem. Involved is human health.

The American people must understand somehow that *Silent Spring*, which they read so avidly, is not a balanced account of the place of pesticides in the world. They must know that its conclusions are not endorsed by the vast majority of scientists and physicians with the background to judge. They must realize that it is a polemic, not a prophecy.

Of course, pesticides are poisonous. They must be treated with respect. They must be kept out of children's way and must never be stored in an unlabeled container—especially never in a milk bottle or a soda bottle. They should be applied only in the way the label says and in accordance with instructions.

But there is no reason to refrain from using them if their use is clearly called for. It would be tragic, for instance, to let the conditions for an insect-borne epidemic arise simply because of vague fears over the possible adverse side effects of pesticides.

There is no evidence that the small amounts of chemical residues found in human tissues have any effect on human health. The average life expectancy has increased twenty years since 1910 and nine years since 1940, and the trend seems to be continuing. Whenever a case of pesticide poisoning occurs, its symptoms are clearly marked and are closely associated with the exposure. There is no indication that pesticides are responsible for cancer or leukemia or any other disease. And happily, there are signs that research will soon find a way to reduce greatly the poisonous effects that do sometimes occur when pesticides are improperly used.

While pesticides in some forest and agricultural uses have unfortunately killed fish and wildlife, this has been built up out of all proportion. Pesticide applications cover such a small part of the land supporting wildlife that the vast majority is completely unaffected. Where pesticides are used, wildlife losses are mostly temporary. Indeed, the areas where pesticides are used most heavily support a thriving wildlife population, with some kinds of birds reaching such numbers that they are serious pests and must be controlled.

I repeat, if it were possible to do without pesticides, every farmer, processor, forester, public-health worker, warehouseman, and gardener would gladly leave them alone. Pesticides cost money, and nobody uses a potentially hazardous chemical for its own sake.

But while research into other ways of controlling the insects and other creatures that man regards as pests has shown great promise, it is clear that it will be many, many years at best before pesticidal chemicals are no longer required. A century of accelerating research has found nonchemical ways to control a few pests and diseases. But our farms and forests still abound with enemies that will seize the slightest chance to lay waste entire woodlands and crops, and endanger the public health. The weapons we have for coping with these foes must not be laid aside until the hoped-for nonchemical weapons are ready to take their place.

Dee Belveal, in an article appearing in the February, 1966, issue of *Today's Health,* published by the American Medical Association, probably put the magnitude of this problem in excellent perspective. I quote in part:

§

People are much concerned these days with the threat of nuclear warfare; the fear that mankind may be destroyed and this planet blown into dust by the hydrogen bomb. The concern is well justified, and yet there is another threat to survival that is almost as dreadful and much closer. The danger does not await the poised finger of an irresponsible dictator; it is not held in abeyance by diplomats around a conference table, nor by threat of retaliation. . . .

The enemy is already here—in the skies, in the fields, and waterways. It is dug into every square foot of our earth; it has invaded homes, schoolhouses, public buildings; it has poisoned food and water; it brings sickness and death by germ warfare to countless millions of people every year. . . .

The enemy within—these walking, crawling, jumping,

flying pests destroy more crops than drought and floods. They destroy more buildings than fire. They are responsible for many of the most dreaded diseases of man and his domestic animals: malaria, yellow fever, dengue, sleeping sickness, and many others. Twenty-one classifications of insects are now in active existence. Some of them eat or attack everything man owns or produces—including man himself. . . .

Of the two million deaths recorded in the United States in a recent 12-month period, insects were the direct or indirect killers in an estimated 60 per cent of them:

1. As direct carriers of the disease.
2. As carriers of pathogenic microorganisms.
3. As indispensable hosts (or incubators) and transmitters of the specific pathogen to man.

As distributors of non-fatal infections and systemic illness, insects have no important competitors. In the words of one famous epidemiologist, "If people understod the mortal danger buzzing around the kitchen on the body of a housefly, they'd do nothing else until it was dead. . . ."

The fight will not be over until we no longer read of deaths from such insect diseases as encephalitis, until bridges and buildings are safe from structural wreckers, and the farmer is freed of the insect threat. If the pests have their way this will never happen. . . .

As technology advances, we must not endanger our health or our food supply because new, ultrasensitive methods of chemical analysis can now detect slight residues of pesticides where none could be detected before. The concepts of "negligible residue" and "permissible residue," recommended by a special committee of the National Academy of Sciences—National Research Council, must be adopted as the basis for enforcement action without delay. Any analytical methods must not be changed without due notice. If legislation is needed to clarify the situation, it should be enacted without delay.

The agencies of the government must take care not

to arouse public alarm without adequate reason. American growers should never again be subjected to such a fiasco as the cranberry incident. Where producers of agricultural commodities are guilty of gross mishandling of materials they should be penalized, and every effort should be made to guard Americans' health and their confidence in the integrity of their food supply. But the innocent must not be made to suffer.

Moreover, the government agencies should continue to improve their cooperation in matters relating to pesticides. The relations of several agencies reached a deplorably low point on this issue a few years ago. Since then there has been some improvement, but there must be more. Perhaps an increased awareness of duty to the American people as a whole, not just a particular agency or interest, would help toward this end.

These steps should do much to restore a balanced climate for pesticides and their makers and users. Otherwise, there are reasons to believe that manufacturers will turn more or less unconsciously to other products whose promise of return is greater and whose marketing involves fewer problems in public relations. As matters stand now, it has been years since a good chemical pesticide has been developed. Meanwhile, insects are developing immunity to some of the ones now in use. Until foolproof ways are found to prevent insects from detoxifying these materials, a succession of insecticides seems to be the only answer. Otherwise we may find ourselves where we were before the arrival of DDT, lacking an essential weapon to oppose a return of malaria in Viet Nam or at home.

We must continue research in many fields, including pesticide research so that we may protect our health and keep our farm plant efficient and ready to meet the demands which will be put upon it, both here and abroad. As I have tried to make plain, in our fight with Communism our agriculture is perhaps our greatest asset. Its scope embraces both national security and national health.

We must not permit anyone or any group to saddle our sources of food and fiber with the burden of the unknown. We must not restrict the use of our best weapons against insect-borne diseases. We must abolish once and for all time this effort to force the doctor, the home gardener, the homemaker, the florist, and those engaged in agriculture to prove that their tools and working materials do not cause that for which even our best researchers, physicians, and scientists do not know the cause.

We must be ready with new weapons and new methods; but in the meantime we must not give up those we have. If we do not follow this policy, we can get ready to say farewell to our high level of living.

Both sides of the story must be told. The overwhelming number of Americans living in the towns and cities, including sportsmen, must become aware of the fact that they are heavily dependent on the latest and best chemical pesticides. We must get the public to accept the fact that man's ingenuity seems limitless.

Truly, when finite quantities of chemical residue equivalent to a dime in a budget of a $100 billion or a second of time in thirty-three thousand years can be isolated and identified, there appears to be no limit to what man can do. It may be true that man will soon be able to detect the disturbance of the earth's surface lingering on from the San Francisco earthquake or the traces of carbon remaining in the atmosphere from the great Chicago fire!

But the development of these advanced testing methods should not mislead us, or cause us to restrict the use of chemicals where there is no evidence of harm if properly used.

We subscribe to the reference to *Silent Spring* which appeared on the wall of the auditorium of the University of California at Davis, and which I have already quoted, "One controversial book has jolted us into re-evaluating man's entire relationship within his environment." But let us pledge that we will accept the facts, but not the fantasy, of *Silent Spring*.

The general public must be made to realize that man's environment is a combination of everything that has gone before and that it will continue to be changed. For as I stated in the beginning, as man has gone along, day by day, year by year, throughout history, he has continued to change and to build for himself a synthetic environment—his clothing, his housing, his food, in fact, almost everything about him is the result of converting natural elements into products of use to him.

Man should not expect miracles, nor worry about the minute traces of minor elements that his ingenuity enables him to identify. Rather, he should interest himself in what is significant. It is not how little can be measured but the effect that counts.

We must remember that all the chemicals used against insects, pests, and diseases have some toxicity; otherwise, they would have no effect. The real concern and sole objective must be to keep toxicity at safe levels, without sacrificing the means of protecting public health, the comfort and convenience of the housewife and the homeowner. We must require standard tests to determine "legal" tolerance, for there is no such thing, in reality, as "zero" tolerance. Legal tolerance must be no greater than the amount which has been determined by responsible agencies to be absolutely safe for use. Such tolerance should not be reduced by each new method of detection, particularly when the residue determined may be as little as three parts in a trillion. We must realize that though each new test "may answer some of the 'whys' of the riddle of life," as sought by Miss Carson in her book, *The Sea Around Us*, such minute quantities of residue certainly do not constitute a danger to life and health.

We must use all our known weapons, as we spend millions of dollars annually in our efforts to find new ones, if we are to enable man to keep that important one step ahead in his continuing contest with insects and disease, with pest and pestilence.

To this end we need public understanding, that we may continue to add to the years of our lives, indeed, THAT WE MAY LIVE!

APPENDIX

When the Surveys and Investigations Staff of the Committee on Appropriations, House of Representatives, was preparing its report on the effects of the use of agricultural pesticides on public health, it interviewed over 185 outstanding scientists and 23 physicians. After the report was made public these experts were asked if they were agreeable to being identified as having been interviewed by the staff. The names of those approving appear below, as listed in the Congressional Record of Tuesday, April 26, 1966.

Dr. R. J. Anderson, Deputy Administrator, Agricultural Research Service, Department of Agriculture, Washington, D. C.

Dr. Robert J. Anderson, Assistant Surgeon General and Chief, Bureau of State Services, Public Health Service, Department of Health, Education and Welfare, Washington, D. C.

Dr. F. S. Arant, Head, Department of Zoology-Entomology, School of Agriculture, Auburn University, Auburn, Alabama

Dr. Alfred W. Avens, Professor of Chemistry, New York State College of Agriculture, Cornell University, Ithaca, New York

Dr. Daniel Banes, Food and Drug Administration, Department of Health, Education and Welfare, Washington, D. C.

Mr. W. F. Barthel, Plant Pest Control Division, Agricultural Research Service, Department of Agriculture, Gulfport, Mississippi

Dr. Warren B. Battle, Chairman, Department of Soils and Crops, College of Agriculture, Rutgers—The State University, New Brunswick, New Jersey

217

Mr. A. H. Baumhover, Tobacco Insects Laboratory, Oxford, North Carolina

Dr. E. W. Beck, Entomology Research Division, Agricultural Research Service, Department of Agriculture, Tifton, Georgia

Dr. Frederick Bellinger, Chief, Chemical Sciences and Materials Division, Engineering Experiment Station, Georgia Institute of Technology, Atlanta, Georgia

Dr. W. L. Bendix, State Veterinarian, Commonwealth of Virginia, Richmond, Virginia

Dr. Morton Beroza, Entomology Research Division, Agricultural Research Service, Department of Agricultural, Beltsville, Maryland

Dr. Frank R. Blood, Professor of Biochemistry and Director of Clinical Laboratories, Central Laboratory Administration, Vanderbilt University Hospital, Nashville, Tennessee

Dr. Alexej B. Borkovec, Entomology Research Division, Agricultural Research Service, Department of Agriculture, Beltsville, Maryland

Professor James L. Brann, Jr., Department of Entomology and Limnology, New York State College of Agriculture, Cornell University, Ithaca, New York

Dr. Andrew W. Breidenbach, Division of Water Supply and Pollution Control, Public Health Service, Department of Health, Education and Welfare, Cincinnati, Ohio

Dr. M. Alice Brown, Department of Public Health, State of California Health and Welfare Agency, Berkeley, California

Dr. Marvin Brunson, Field Station, Department of Agriculture, Moorestown, New Jersey

Dr. Philip A. Butler, Director, Biological Laboratory, Bureau of Commercial Fisheries, Fish and Wildlife Service, Department of the Interior, Gulf Breeze, Florida

Dr. T. C. Byerly, Administrator, Cooperative State Research Service, Department of Agriculture, Washington, D. C.

Dr. G. M. Cairns, Dean of Agriculture, University of Maryland, College Park, Maryland

Dr. Douglas G. Campbell, Physician, Suite 720-490 Post Street, San Francisco, California

Dr. J. E. Campbell, Milk and Food Research, Public Health Service, Department of Health, Education and Welfare,

Robert A. Taft Sanitary Engineering Center, Cincinnati, Ohio

Dr. G. E. Carman, Chairman, Department of Entomology, College of Agriculture, University of California, Riverside, California

Dr. Howard L. Carnahan, Crops Research Division, Agricultural Research Service, Department of Agriculture, University of Nevada, Reno, Nevada.

Professor P. J. Chapman, Head, Department of Entomology, Cornell University, New York State College of Agriculture, Geneva, New York

Mr. Huston V. Claborn, Pesticide Chemicals Research, Department of Agriculture Laboratory, Kerrville, Texas

Dr. M. R. Clarkson, President, American Veterinary Medical Association, Washington, D. C.

Dr. J. W. Clayton, The Du Pont Company, Inc., Wilmington, Delaware

Dr. George D. Coffee, Chief, Bureau of Milk Control, District of Columbia Department of Public Health, Washington, D. C.

Dr. Donald L. Collins, New York State Science Service, New York, New York

Dr. Oliver B. Cope, Bureau of Sport Fisheries and Wildlife, Fish and Wildlife Service, Department of the Interior, Denver, Colorado

Dr. H. C. Cox, Director, Southern Grain Insects Research Laboratory, Entomology Research Division, Agricultural Research Service, Department of Agriculture, Tifton, Georgia

Dr. Donald G. Crosby, Chairman, Agricultural Toxicology and Residue Research Laboratory, University of California, Davis, California

Dr. Edwin A. Crosby, Assistant Director, Raw Products Research Bureau, National Canners Association, Berkeley, California

Dr. Chester E. Cross, University of Massachusetts, Agricultural Experiment Station, Cranberry Station, East Wareham, Massachusetts

Dr. Jack M. Curtis, Food and Drug Administration, Department of Health, Education and Welfare, Washington, D. C.

Dr. R. A. Damon, Jr., Amherst College, Amherst, Massachusetts

Dr. William J. Darby, Division of Nutrition, Departments of

Medicine and Biochemistry, Vanderbilt University, Nashville, Tennessee

Dr. Edward Davens, Deputy Commissioner, Department of Health, State of Maryland, Baltimore, Maryland

Dr. T. S. Davich, Director, Boll Weevil Research Laboratory, Entomology Research Division, Agricultural Research Service, Department of Agriculture, State College, Mississippi

Dr. John E. Davies, Director, Community Studies on Pesticides, Dade County Department of Public Health, Miami, Florida

Dr. Joseph H. Davis, Dade County Medical Examiner, Miami, Florida

Dr. George C. Decker, Principal Scientist and Head, Section of Economic Entomology, Department of Registration and Education, Illinois Natural History Survey, Urbana, Illinois

Dr. William B. Deickmann, Professor of Pharmacology and Director of Research and Teaching Center of Toxicology, School of Medicine, University of Miami, Coral Gables, Florida

Dr. James E. Dewey, Extension Program Leader, Chemicals—Pesticides, New York State Cooperative Extension Service, Comstock Hall, Ithaca, New York

Dr. S. C. Dorman, Associate Director, Biological Research Center, Stauffer Chemical Company Company, Mountain View, California

Dr. H. L. Dunton, Head, Department of Agronomy, Virginia Polytechnic Institute, Blacksburg, Virginia

Dr. William F. Durham, Scientist Director, Chief, Wenatchee Field Station, Communicable Disease Center, Public Health Service, Department of Health, Education and Welfare, Wenatchee, Washington

Dr. E. H. Dustman, Director, Patuxent Wildlife Research Center, Bureau of Sport Fisheries and Wildlife, Fish and Wildlife Service, Department of the Interior, Laurel, Maryland

Dr. Gaines W. Eddy, Entomology Research Division, Agricultural Research Service, Department of Agriculture, Corvallis, Oregon

Dr. Amy C. Einert, University of California, Berkeley, California

Dr. R. W. Engel, Head, Department of Biochemistry and Nutrition, College of Agriculture, Virginia Polytechnic Institute, Blacksburg, Virginia

Dr. Raymond A. Evans, Crops Research Division, Agricultural Research Service, Department of Agriculture, University of Nevada, Reno, Nevada

Dr. Hans L. Falk, Chief, Carcinogenesis Studies Branch, National Cancer Institute, National Institutes of Health, Department of Health, Education and Welfare, Bethesda, Maryland

Mr. C. C. Fancher, Supervisor, Southern Region, Plant Pest Control Division, Agricultural Research Service, Department of Agriculture, Gulfport, Mississippi

Dr. E. F. Feichtmeir, Manager, Product Application, Agricultural Research Division, Shell Development Company, Modesto, California

Dr. Denzel E. Ferguson, Professor, Department of Zoology, Mississippi State University, State College, Mississippi

Dr. E. E. Flech, Entomology Research Division, Agricultural Research Service, Department of Agriculture, Beltsville, Maryland

Dr. Arthur S. Flemming, President, University of Oregon, Eugene, Oregon

Dr. Milton J. Foter, Assistant Program Officer for Environmental Health, Bureau of State Services, Public Health Service, Department of Health, Education and Welfare, Washington, D. C.

Dr. Virgil H. Freed, Head, Department of Agricultural Chemistry, Agricultural Experiment Station, Oregon State University, Corvallis, Oregon

Dr. O. E. Frye, Jr., Executive Director, Game and Fresh Water Fish Commission, State of Florida, Tallahassee, Florida

Dr. Irwin H. Gilbert, Entomology Research Division, Agricultural Research Service, Department of Agriculture, Gainesville, Florida

Dr. G. C. Graf, Professor of Dairy Science, Virginia Polytechnic Institute, Blacksburg, Virginia

Dr. O. H. Graham, Investigations Leader, Livestock Insects Investigations, Entomology Research Division, Agricultural Research Service, Department of Agriculture, Kerrville, Texas

Dr. James McD. Grayson, Head, Department of Entomology,

College of Agriculture, Virginia Polytechnic Institute, Blacksburg, Virginia

Dr. George G. Grisco, Professor of Entomology, New York State College of Agriculture, Cornell University, Ithaca, New York

Dr. Robert M. Grodner, Louisiana State University, Baton Rouge, Louisiana

Dr. Alfred R. Grzenda, Assistant Chief, Land Drainage Studies, Southeast Water Laboratory, Department of Health, Education and Welfare, Athens, Georgia

Dr. F. A. Gunther, Professor of Entomology and Chemist, College of Agriculture, Agricultural Experiment Station, University of California, Riverside, California

Dr. Gordon Guyer, Michigan State University, East Lansing, Michigan

Mr. Stanley Hall, Pesticide Chemical Research Division, Agricultural Research Service, Department of Agriculture, Beltsville, Maryland

Dr. H. L. Haller, Office of Administrator, Agricultural Research Service, Department of Agriculture, Washington, D. C.

Mr. Roy Hansberry, Assistant Director, Agricultural Research Division, Shell Development Company, Modesto, California

Dr. Thomas H. Harris, Pesticides Regulation Division, Agricultural Research Service, Department of Agriculture, Washington, D. C.

Dr. Kirby L. Hays, Professor of Zoology-Entomology, School of Agriculture and Agricultural Experiment Station System, Auburn University, Auburn, Alabama

Dr. Wayland J. Hays, Jr., Medical Director, Chief, Toxicology Section, Communicable Disease Center, Department of Health, Education and Welfare, Atlanta, Georgia

Dr. Andrew Hedmeg, Louisiana State Board of Health, New Orleans, Louisiana

Dr. A. M. Heimpel, Principal Insect Pathologist, Insect Pathology Laboratory, Entomology Research Division, Agricultural Research Service, Department of Agriculture, Beltsville, Maryland

Dr. H. E. O. Heineman, Vice President, Pet Milk Company, Saint Louis, Missouri

Mr. William F. Helms, Inspector, Plant Pest Control Division, Agricultural Research Service, Department of Agriculture, Greenville, Mississippi

Dr. C. H. Hine, Consultant in Occupational Medicine and Industrial Toxicology, University of California Medical Center, San Francisco, California

Mr. J. D. Hoffman, Tobacco Insects Laboratory, Oxford, North Carolina

Dr. C. H. Hoffmann, Associate Director, Entomology Research Division, Agricultural Research Service, Department of Agriculture, Beltsville, Maryland

Dr. Joseph Holmes, University of Colorado Medical School, Denver, Colorado

Dr. James G. Horsfall, Director, Connecticut Agricultural Experiment Station, New Haven, Connecticut

Dr. Henry F. Howe, American Medical Association, Chicago, Illinois

Dr. C. E. Howes, Head, Department of Poultry Science, College of Agriculture, Virginia Polytechnic Institute, Blacksburg, Virginia

Dr. Carl B. Huffaker, Professor of Entomology, College of Agriculture, and Entomologist, Agricultural Experiment Station, University of California, Berkeley, California

Dr. Hugh H. Hussey, American Medical Association, Chicago, Illinois

Dr. Ross E. Hutchins, Entomologist, State Plant Board of Mississippi, State College, Mississippi

Dr. Don D. Irish, Executive Research, The Dow Chemical Company, Midland, Michigan

Dr. Martin Jacobson, Entomology Research Division, Agricultural Research Service, Department of Agriculture, Beltsville Maryland

Dr. William H. James, Louisiana State University, Baton Rouge, Louisiana

Dr. W. R. Jenkins, Professor, Department of Entomology and Economic Zoology, College of Agriculture, Rutgers—The State University, New Brunswick, New Jersey

Dr. Daniel Jobbine, Rutgers—The State University, New Brunswick, New Jersey

Dr. Howard Johnson, Bureau of Food and Chemistry, State of Pennsylvania, Harrisburg, Pennsylvania

Dr. Ogden C. Johnson, Associate Secretary, American Medical Association, Chicago, Illinois

Dr. Raymond E. Johnson, Assistant Director, Sport Fisheries and Wildlife Bureau, Fish and Wildlife Service, Department of the Interior, Washington, D. C.

Dr. H. G. Johnston, Entomologist, Division of Production and Marketing, National Cotton Council of America, Memphis, Tennessee

Dr. G. C. Kent, Professor and Head, Department of Plant Pathology, New York State College of Agriculture, Cornell University, Ithaca, New York

Dr. M. L. Keplinger, Toxicologist, Department of Pharmacology and the Research and Teaching Center of Toxicology, School of Medicine, University of Miami, Coral Gables, Florida

Dr. Wendell W. Kilgore, University of California, Davis, California

Dr. John A. King, Manager, Research and Development, Agricultural Division, American Cynamid Company, Princeton, New Jersey

Dr. Vernon Knight, Clinical Director, National Institute of Allergy and Infectious Diseases, National Institutes of Health, Department of Health, Education and Welfare, Bethesda, Maryland

Dr. E. F. Knipling, Director, Entomology Research Division, Agricultural Research Service, Department of Agriculture, Beltsville, Maryland

Dr. Harold C. Knoblauch, Associate Administrator, Cooperative State Research Service, Department of Agriculture, Washington, D. C.

Dr. Paul Kotin, Associate Director for Field Studies, National Cancer Institute, National Institutes of Health, Department of Health, Education and Welfare, Washington, D. C.

Dr. Herman F. Kraybill, Bureau of State Services, Public Health Service, Department of Health, Education and Welfare, Washington, D. C.

Professor J. W. Kuzmeski, University of Massachusetts, North Hatfield, Massachusetts

Mr. J. J. Lamb, Tobacco Insects Laboratory, Oxford, North Carolina

Dr. K. Lampe, University of Miami, Coral Gables, Florida

Dr. R. E. Larson, Dean of the College of Agriculture, Pennsylvania State University, University Park, Pennsylvania

Dr. Gerald Lauers, Aquatic Biologist, Public Health Service, Department of Health, Education and Welfare, Athens, Georgia

Dr. Arnold Lehman, Food and Drug Administration, Department of Health, Education and Welfare, Washington, D. C.

Dr. Allen B. Lemmon, Chief, Division of Plant Industry, Department of Agriculture, State of California, Sacramento, California

Dr. A. Starker Leopold, Professor of Zoology, Museum of Vertebrate Zoology, University of California, Berkeley, California

Dr. John R. Lewis, Associate Director, Department of Drugs, American Medical Association, Chicago, Illinois

Dr. Paul C. Lippold, Professor of Entomology, New York State College of Agriculture, Cornell University, Ithaca, New York

Dr. Donald J. Lisk, Professor of Pesticidal Chemistry, New York State College of Agriculture, Cornell University, Ithaca, New York

Dr. W. K. Lowen, The Du Pont Company, Inc., Wilmington, Delaware

Dr. Joseph A. Luizzo, Louisiana State University, Baton Rouge, Louisiana

Dr. William MacDonald, University of Miami, Coral Gables, Florida

Dr. K. E. Marple, Director, Agricultural Research Division, Shell Development Company, Modesto, California

Dr. Fred O. Marzke, Communicable Disease Center, Savannah, Georgia

Dr. J. G. Matthyse, Professor of Public Administration, New York State College of Agriculture, Cornell University, Ithaca, New York

Dr. Edward McGovran, Cooperative State Research Service, Department of Agriculture, Washington, D. C.

Mr. Thomas McIntyre, Supervisory Entomologist, Plant Pest

Control Division, Agricultural Research Service, Department of Agriculture, Otis Air Force Base, Massachusetts

Dr. Robert L. Metcalf, Professor of Entomology, Office of the Vice-Chancellor, Academic Affairs, University of California, Riverside, California

Dr. James W. Miles, Assistant Chief, Biology/Chemistry Section, Public Health Service, Department of Health, Education and Welfare, Savannah, Georgia

Mr. John H. Milner, III, Entomologist, Plant Pest Control Division, Agricultural Research Service, Department of Agriculture, Otis Air Force Base, Massachusetts

Dr. Donald I. Mount, Division of Water Supply and Pollution Control, Public Health Service, Department of Health, Education and Welfare, Cincinnati, Ohio

Dr. Emil M. Mrak, Chancellor, University of California, Davis, California

Dr. Arthur A. Muka, Professor of Entomology, New York State College of Agriculture, Cornell University, Ithaca, New York

Dr. J. A. Nagale, Head, Department of Entomology, Field Station, Waltham, Massachusetts

Dr. A. A. Nelson, Food and Drug Administration, Department of Health, Education and Welfare, Washington, D. C.

Dr. L. D. Newsom, Head, Department of Entomology, Louisiana State University and Agricultural and Mechanical College, Baton Rouge, Louisiana

Dr. H. Page Nicholson, Chief, Land Drainage Studies, Southeast Water Laboratory, Department of Health, Education and Welfare, Athens, Georgia

Dr. Arthur F. Novak, Professor and Chairman, Department of Food Science and Technology, Louisiana State University, Baton Rouge, Louisiana

Dr. Bernard L. Oser, President, Food and Drug Research Laboratories, Inc., Maspeth, New York

Dr. Charles E. Palm, Dean, New York State College of Agriculture, Cornell University, Ithaca, New York

Dr. R. M. Parry, Chief, Dairy Division, Department of Agriculture and Natural Resources, State of Connecticut, Hartford, Connecticut

Dr. George W. Pearce, Chief, Biology/Chemistry Section, Technology Branch, Communicable Disease Center, Department of Health, Education and Welfare, Savannah, Georgia

Dr. M. L. Peterson, University Dean of Agriculture, Director, Agricultural Experiment Station, University of California, Berkeley, California

Dr. R. D. Radeleff, Veterinarian in Charge, Animal Disease and Parasite Research Division, Agricultural Research Service, Department of Agriculture, Kerrville, Texas

Dr. J. L. Radomski, Professor of Pharmacology, School of Medicine, University of Miami, Coral Gables, Florida

Dr. Jack W. Ralls, Research Coordinator, National Canners Association, Berkeley, California

Dr. Stacy B. Randle, State Chemist, College of Agriculture, New Jersey Agricultural Experiment Station, Rutgers—The State University, New Brunswick, New Jersey

Dr. Theron G. Randolph, Physician, 720 North Michigan Avenue, Chicago, Illinois

Dr. J. P. Reed, Associate Research Specialist, Department of Entomology and Economic Zoology, College of Agriculture, Rutgers—The State University, New Brunswick, New Jersey

Dr. William E. Ribelin, Pathologist, Central Medical Department, Environmental Health Laboratory, American Cyanamid Company, Princeton, New Jersey

Dr. Roy E. Ritts, Jr., Physician, American Medical Association, Education and Research Foundation, Chicago, Illinois

Dr. William E. Robbins, Principal Insect Physiologist, Entomology Research Division, Agricultural Research Service, Department of Agriculture, Beltsville, Maryland

Dr. William Rogoff, U.S. Department of Agriculture, Corvallis, Oregon

Dr. Aaron A. Rosen, In Charge, Organic Contaminants Unit, Chemistry and Physics, Basic and Applied Sciences Branch, Division of Water Supply and Pollution Control, Department of Health, Education and Welfare, Cincinnati, Ohio

Mr. V. K. Rowe, Biochemical Research Laboratory, The Dow Chemical Company, Midland, Michigan

Mr. Boyd L. Samuels, Director, Harmful Residue Laboratory, Department of Agriculture, Commonwealth of Virginia, Richmond, Virginia

Dr. Mary L. Schafer, Research Chemist, Food Chemistry, Public Health Service, Department of Health, Education and Welfare, Cincinnati, Ohio

Dr. Milton Schechter, Pesticide Chemicals Research Branch, Department of Agriculture, Greenbelt, Maryland

Mr. D. J. Schliessman, Public Health Service, Department of Health, Education and Welfare, Atlanta, Georgia

Dr. H. F. Schoof, Biology/Chemistry Section, Technology Branch, Communicable Disease Center, Department of Health, Education and Welfare, Savannah, Georgia

Dr. D. R. Shepherd, Associate Director, Plant Pest Control Division, Agricultural Research Service, Department of Agriculture, Hyattsville, Maryland

Dr. S. W. Simmons, Scientist Director, Chief, Technology Branch, Communicable Disease Center, Department of Health, Education and Welfare, Atlanta, Georgia

Dr. Ray F. Smith, Chairman, Department of Entomology and Parasitology, College of Agriculture, University of California, Berkeley, California

Dr. Ira I. Somers, Director, Research Laboratories, National Canners Association, Washington, D. C.

Dr. H. C. Spencer, Biochemical Research Laboratory, The Dow Chemical Company, Midland, Michigan

Dr. A. John Speziale, Director of Research, Agricultural Division, Monsanto Company, St. Louis, Missouri

Dr. A. A. Spielman, Dean and Director, College of Agriculture, University of Massachusetts, Amherst, Massachusetts

Mr. James M. Stanley, Agricultural Engineer, Agricultural Engineering Research Division, Agricultural Research Service, Department of Agriculture, Blacksburg, Virginia

Dr. Frederick J. Stare, School of Nutrition, Harvard University, Cambridge, Massachusetts

Dr. Frank L. Stark, Jr., Plant Industry Research and Development, American Cyanamid Company, Princeton, New Jersey

Dr. Ordway Starnes, Director, New Jersey Agricultural Experiment Station, Rutgers—The State University, New Brunswick, New Jersey

Dr. A. W. Steers, Food and Drug Administration, Department of Health, Education and Welfare, Washington, D. C.

Dr. Allen Steinhauer, University of Maryland, College Park, Maryland

Dr. Edward A. Steinhaus, Dean, Division of Biological Sciences, University of California, Irvine, California

Dr. Richard D. Stewart, Director, Medical Research Division, The Dow Chemical Company, Midland, Michigan

Mr. Robert D. Sweet, Professor of Vegetable Crops, New York State College of Agriculture, Cornell University, Ithaca, New York

Dr. John E. Swift, Extension Entomologist, Statewide Coordinator—Pesticides, Agricultural Extension Service, University of California, Berkeley, California

Dr. Clarence M. Tarzwell, Chief, Aquatic Biology Section, Basic and Applied Sciences Branch, Division of Water Supply and Pollution Control, Department of Health, Education and Welfare, Cincinnati, Ohio

Dr. Carlton F. Taylor, Professor and Chairman, Plant Pathology Extension, Cooperative Extension Service, Pennsylvania State University, University Park, Pennsylvania

Dr. James G. Telfer, Director, Department of Environmental Health, American Medical Association, Chicago, Illinois

Dr. Yashura Tonada, Professor of Insect Pathology, University of California, Berkeley, California

Dr. David C. Tudor, Research Specialist in Poultry Pathology, Department of Animal Sciences, College of Agriculture, Rutgers—The State University, New Brunswick, New Jersey

Mr. Neely Turner, Assistant Director and State Entomologist, Connecticut Agricultural Experiment Station, New Haven, Connecticut

Mr. Kenneth C. Walker, Assistant to Deputy Administrator, Agricultural Research Service, Department of Agriculture, Washington, D. C.

Dr. Leon W. Weinberger, Chief, Basic and Applied Sciences Branch, Division of Water Supply and Pollution Control, Department of Health, Education and Welfare, Washington, D. C.

Dr. Irma West, California Department of Health, Berkeley, California

Dr. William E. Westlake, Department of Entomology, University of California, Riverside, California

Dr. Ellsworth H. Wheeler, Amherst University, Amherst, Massachusetts

Dr. James R. Whitley, Supervisor, Water Quality Investigations, Missouri Conservation Commission, Columbia Fisheries Laboratory, Jefferson City, Missouri

Dr. Billy Ray Wilson, Chairman, Bureau of Conservation and Environmental Science, College of Agriculture, Rutgers—The State University, New Brunswick, New Jersey

Mr. Homer R. Wolfe, Public Health Service, Department of Health, Education and Welfare, Wenatchee, Washington

Dr. Charles B. Wood, Associate Professor of Food Technology in Horticulture, Virginia Polytechnic Intitute, Blacksburg, Virginia

Dr. John F. Yost, Director, Product Development and Registrations, Agricultural Division, American Cyanamid Company, Princeton, New Jersey

Dr. John A. Zapp, Jr., The Du Pont Company, Inc., Wilmington, Delaware

Dr. Mitchell R. Zavon, Associate Professor of Industrial Medicine, Kettering Laboratory, University of Cincinnati, and Assistant Health Commissioner, City of Cincinnati, Cincinnati, Ohio

Dr. Gunter Zweig, Chemist, College of Agriculture, Agricultural Experiment Station, University of California, Davis, California

INDEX

Acaricides, 10
Acarids, 49-50
Accidents, 81, 84-86, 90, 130
Acreage treated:
  herbicides, 196
  pesticides, 128
Act:
  Federal Food, Drug, and Cosmetic Act, 36
  Federal Insecticide, Fungicide, and Rodenticide Act, 36
  Federal Water Pollution Control, 164
Adenoma, in rats, 96
Adjuvants, 21
African sleeping sickness, 49
Agricultural commodities, 37, 38
Agricultural experiment stations, 9, 36, 117
Agricultural extension service, 60, 75, 149
Agricultural Research Service, 36, 197-198
Agriculture:
  acreage treated, 128
  benefits from, 1-5
  evolution, 1-2
  importance, 208-209, 214
  intensive, 16-17
  opposition to new methods, 15
  political weakness, 208
  practices, 9-10
  primitive, 1, 16, 20

  production, 4, 7-8
  size as an industry, 8
Agriculture, Department of:
  Appropriations Committee investigation, 124-125
  crop improvement, 9
  Federal Pest Control Board, representation, 74
  fish kills, 162-166
  information services, 75-76, 204-205
  insect control:
    fumigants, 56
    insecticides, 147
    other than insecticidal, 68, 74-75, 125, 129, 183-207, 211
  interagency coordination, 148-149, 161-166, 179, 205
  Orlando, Florida, laboratory, 47, 83
  pesticides:
    development, 22, 33
    hearings, 125, 163-166
    monitoring, 65-67, 103, 201
    policy, 148-149
    registration, 36-39, 144, 147-148
    regulation, 36-38, 124, 150, 151-152, 170, 193
  research:
    plant disease control, 195-196, 197-198

231